CW00537529

VERY MUCH ALIVE

Stories of Resilience

Edited by Lexie Angelo

More from The Selkie Publications CIC

States of Transformation
The Same Havoc

ACKNOWLEDGEMENTS

Chief Editor
Lexie Angelo

Prose Editors
Sam Le Butt, Christa Marie, Sonali Misra

Poetry Editors
Stefano Paparo, Chelsea Welsh

Production
Taliha Quadri

Cover Artist
Pranisha Shrestha

THE SELKIE PUBLICATIONS CIC
Unit 5, 241a Selbourne Road
Luton, Bedfordshire, LU4 8NP

contact@theselkie.co.uk

The moral rights of the authors have been asserted.

First published in 2020 by Lexie Angelo on behalf of The Selkie Publications CIC.

All rights reserved. No part of this publication may be reproduced, stored in a retrieval system or transmitted in any form or by any means, electronic, mechanical, photocopying, recording or otherwise without the prior permission of the publisher.

The publication of this anthology has been generously supported by Calgary Arts Development.

This selection copyright © 2020 The Selkie Publications CIC

FIC003000 FICTION / Anthologies (multiple authors)

ISBN 978 1 7770865 2 7

Typeset in Sabon LT

Printed in Canada

theselkie.co.uk

CONTENTS

Lexie Angelo

Introduction

When I first considered the theme of resiliency for this book, the word itself didn't evoke a sentimental feeling. At the time, I was busy researching grant funding and I'll admit the term felt closer to a corporate buzzword than an emotional truth. Selecting 'resiliency' as the theme was a quick and benign decision, one I hoped would resonate around the grant funding table first, and eventually within the artists' psyches.

When Calgary Arts Development gave us the green light in 2019, the months ahead were spent diligently reaching out to artists and advertising our call for submissions. I ambitiously wanted representation from all across Canada. I sought to feature writers, poets and artists from coast to coast, from all backgrounds and orientations. And I was thrilled to have my dream manifest; I couldn't wait to share this book with the world.

I had no idea what was about to come.

The global coronavirus pandemic swept through our editorial process and thrust us into uncharted waters. I abandoned all hope of a launch event in 2020, and I had no choice but to request an extension. Our editors, who work from all corners of the world, were facing their own personal obstacles. Some of our team members were in strict lockdowns, others were stuck abroad and trying to return home. I felt scared, worried, frustrated, tired and lonely. I didn't feel resilient. I was drowning in a backlog of emails, working from home unshowered, unloading the dishwasher on Zoom calls, not caring if I was muted or not.

When I first plucked the term out of the corporate vernacular, I thought resilience was akin to slaying a dragon or reaching the peak of an insurmountable mountain. But it turns out, resilience isn't slaying the dragon. It's getting out of bed, combing your hair in the morning and looking at the sword.

At first, I assumed the title of this anthology was going to be the theme I picked all those months ago. It wasn't until our team suggested exploring other title options that I was struck by a phrase in the poem 'Sunrise on a Double-sunned Earth' by Marina Stepanova (page 49). The words caught my eye because I felt they summed up what I had been feeling for months: no matter what restrictions and obstacles I was facing, I was still here, and very much alive. Even though I wondered if our theme was a little too on the nose after all that had happened, I still yearned for the optimism I found in that phrase.

Nevertheless, the pre-pandemic stories you will find in this book don't contain utopias or cast a light back on a better or happier time. They don't tell stories of a world where nothing bad happens. As you'll read, it's the small acts of resiliency that give humans the courage to face their fears and ultimately, to change.

The stories in this collection won't feel unfamiliar. They are the mother silently picking lice out of her daughter's hair, the student asking to be called by a new name, the girl confronting her history of disordered eating, the boy accepting an inevitable disability or the grandmother lamenting the missing and murdered Indigenous women and children. We've nestled these tales by their commonalities such as the natural world, dreams, violence, or motherhood, and many languages shape these expressions.

In these pages you will find artwork, poetry and stories by Canadian artists and our editors. We are part of this journey together, and although we all face different dragons, we are still here and very much alive.

Heather Bonin MacIntosh

When Vicki Shot a Moose

Nonfiction

Stuart calls about the moose. A bull, maybe five years old, is grazing in Vicki's alfalfa field. Vicki can't believe her luck; she renewed her bull tag with Fish and Wildlife two weeks earlier. She drops the plastic laundry basket on the oak kitchen table and heads for the back porch. The guns are by the bathroom, three in a row, locked into place so that their upright barrels stare at a blank ceiling. Unlocking the gun rack, she grabs the .308 Norma Magnum, a gift from her father. The gun is old—World War II era—and heavy, but it fires true and the scope is excellent, with three-and-a-half to ten times the magnification. More power than she needs if the moose stays in her field.

She kicks around the closet until she finds her boots. Her husband's navy snowmobile suit swings toward her and she tugs it free. Dressed, she reaches a hand into the box of shells on the window ledge and extracts six. She inserts four of the bullets into the magazine and drops the other two into her pocket, just in case. When she hunts with her family, her father will load her rifle for her, a small sign of his love that Vicki holds inside her. A metallic ping sounds as she walks to the door. *That's no good.* Scanning the house, she spots the paper towel roll on the counter, wraps the shells carefully within one of the sheets, and returns them to her coat. Her smile spreads as she walks, now silently, to the door. *Damn right a woman can figure things out on her own.*

Outside, the cold snaps at her face and ears. At minus twenty-three with a light windchill, any exposed skin will freeze in fifteen or twenty minutes. This fact runs through her head as she turns back for a toque and rolls up the edges to make a beanie that exposes her ears. She pushes her dark hair back; acute hearing is essential.

Vicki enters the forest and follows an animal trail, her own tracks obliterating smaller ones left by snow hares and deer. Familiar excitement mingles with a tinge of fear—she does not like to hunt alone. The air smells like winter, stale and bland. Further into the woods, the trees emit their spruce and pine scents. It is a slog, wading through this deep snow, and she wishes for long legs like the moose, for a graceless but easy stride. *If Dad could see me now.* He would say nothing, of course, but he would be proud of her, wouldn't he? His girl, on her own, hunting a bull moose, knowing what gear to take and what to leave behind, when to rush and when to wait. Maybe she can make him some sausage if she bags the moose; they could use the meat this winter. Suddenly, she feels tired, worn out from trying to prove her worth to this man who is so damn hard to please.

She stops to rest and listen and lean into the quiet: trees creak in the light wind, a cow moos in the distance, a dog bark-bark-barks. The sounds mask the noise of her movement through the brush. She looks down; her navy snowsuit is not ideal, but it'll do. She remembers a shopper in front of her at the Fish and Game store who asked for a specific pattern of leaves and mosses on his jacket and the most-undetectable hunter's blind. She smirks. Camouflage and gear are rarely the problem. Moose have shitty eyesight; it's your sound and scent that give you away.

Deep snow obscures the path under her feet, but she moves as stealthily as she can. *Crack.* A twig snaps. She freezes and waits, hoping she has not given away her position. Ahead, the alfalfa field lays covered in snow, bunches of grasses poking through in an uneven pattern. She sees a sway of brown between the trees where the moose grazes at the edge of the field in a good location. Her awareness heightened, she cautiously circles left toward a fallen log. Her stance is wide like a football player running through an obstacle course of tires; she will not be discovered by the noise of nylon rubbing together. Her vantage improves with each step, and she sees the bulk of the torso twenty metres ahead. Three steps, listen, two steps, wait, breathe. *Am I good enough?*

She reaches the log unnoticed. The moose nuzzles the snow

and comes up with a mouthful of amber grass. Around Vicki, tree trunks sway and moan; she times her drop to the ground with the creaking, unheard. She is close, maybe too close. Tears well up in her eyes and she blinks quickly. The adrenaline is stronger than she's used to. *It'll screw with your accuracy.*

Patience. It is her father's voice, commanding, teaching, admonishing, steadying.

Her breathing slows. Perching the rifle on the log, she puts a live round in the chamber, closes the bolt and clicks the safety on before double-checking it. The animal in front takes a step back, worsening her angle, so she waits. The sun comes out from behind a cloud, and the snow is suddenly covered in gleaming diamonds. The deciduous trees are beautiful in their starkness—bark prominent, limbs exposed. Stillness infuses her and she becomes a part of the landscape. Everyday cares evaporate in the cool air: no conflicts with coworkers at the bank, no expectations from her husband, no chores waiting to be done. Her calves cramp but she does not move from her cross-legged, meditative state. The minutes stretch until she loses track of time and is caught in a cycle of memories of hunting trips with her mom and dad, uncle and sisters, of the years tromping through bush, the hours sitting behind logs, the days battling cold winds in the fall and mosquitos in the spring.

A magpie caws. The moose raises its snout into the air. Vicki sniffs at her coveralls. Farm. Cow shit and feed and dogs. Human odours, but no different from the scents in the area. She curses her rosemary-and-mint shampoo, then touches the toque, which might be just smelly enough to keep her safe. The moose lifts its nose up and down and takes one step forward.

Carefully, she removes her mittens. Her pulse pounds in her ears; she cannot afford 'buck fever' to overpower her. She talks herself through her preparation, enjoying the challenge of controlling her own reaction and breathing. *Hold the rifle tight to keep it as steady as you can*, her father's voice says. She pushes her shoulder into the butt of the gun. She must not fail.

The mooses's head jerks upward and she pulls the trigger. The kickback knocks her off balance, but she barely notices. Muscle memory takes over as she unloads the empty casing and puts in another live shell without thinking. She sits up and re-aims, but there is no need. The moose staggers three paces and falls into the snow. On her feet again, she edges toward the wounded animal. The bull struggles to rise, then its legs crumple and it twitches on the ground. A rush of adrenaline fills her veins. She read somewhere that it releases the same endorphins into the body as a passionate kiss. Kinda true.

Vicki's hands shake as she clicks the safety, leans the rifle against a tree and stoops low. The moose lets out a final shudder and stops moving. As she strokes the hide, tears stream down her cheeks and her nose drips. Birds flap away into the air. Dogs bark in a farm-to-farm chorus. When her tears abate, she shakes the bullets free from the paper towel and wipes her nose and eyes with the cloth. The cold seeps in as the adrenaline wears off, so she warms her hands under her armpits for a few moments. *Breathe*. She scoots around to the back of the animal and snaps a selfie with the moose to post online, where her father will see it.

Moni Brar
1947

*August 1947 saw the partition of British India into the two
separate states of India and Pakistan. It caused the largest mass
migration in human history of 10 million people. More than one
million civilians died in the accompanying riots and fighting,
particularly in the western region of Punjab, which was cut in
two by the new border.*

you see, there's you and there's me.
your grandfather came
reeking of manifest destiny, disdain and desire.
he raped a heathen,
and hazel eyes suddenly appear in my family.

new lines drawn on old territory, on my sacred land,
by your Crown, your Queen.
new lines etched within people,
Hindus Muslims Sikhs partitioned
into nations whose names they could not spell.

proud Sikh men unsheathed kirpans,
slit open their wives and daughters
from chin to abdomen
to protect their *ijit*, their honour,
from the touch of Muslim warriors.

streets awash with blood,
neighbour turned upon neighbour,
blazing bodies and huts and hopes
lit up the sky.
these are the stories my people tell me,

the stories I'm born into.
tiny time

bombs go off
like snowballs
hitting the back of my head,
explosions of thought snap me in half,
splinter me once again,
transport me to a time I was not in.

Alycia Pirmohamed
Arrivals

I learned this story through the apricot
slices and golden raisins
you fed me at mosque.

Arrival meant many things
but always seemed to look like
plant roots upending the soil—

a chaos that disappeared once in a while
underneath a charge of snow.
I know arrival really meant

A young girl reckoning her first
boreal green eclipse, one spruce tree
in front of another

and another, and another—
tending to her first wild rose bush
not unharmed by its thorns—

how arrival disguised itself
within fields of canola
that shone pure gold, as if to say
here you will find peace,

happiness, barakat.
I know that you are still searching.

I can taste the dried fruit
that is your silence
because it is my silence too, Mother.

Sam Le Butt
Ultradark

This time it's close enough to see the plate shards cascading out from their impact with the wall like a sneeze. I don't stay to see where they fall; I'm outta there quick sharp, through the backdoor and across the grave-grey mass-yard. I duck through the hole in the wire fence and then I'm across the plot, huffing like a horse. I should stay and reason with him, keep him off the others, hold him down like Dad used to, but he's tried and got big since the work shrivelled up, injecting time and bubbling out in elaborate colours like the rest of the young men running around the Outskirts that call each other (Boy). Nothing in his brain about the balloons growing in our bellies.

There are no stars tonight—never any stars—and I storm forward into the ultradark, wiping the not-tears from my face, half-mixed with sweat from the saggy heat. I don't need to look back to know his face is swinging in the doorframe like a mask in the wind.

I turn at the tree I've turned at so many times I don't even have to count the blight spots anymore and into the woods, insults racing through my head at (Boy) and the rest of them in that godforsaken housing—*I hope it burns, I hope they burn, twisted fuckers, useless piece-o-shits*—when I stumble over something big and hot on the ground and almost go flying.

I curse it from palm-heels and knees, all mud and smell on me, then look behind, over my shoulder, at the lump on the ground.

It's still breathing.

I crawl a little closer—if it's a dying rebel, I've gotta get out of here fast before I get slurped up into the fray—but then I see fur (hair?) and I draw up away from it, get it out of my face so I can take stock of its size, its heat. Even in the heavy summer air tonight I can feel *its* heat, its heavily, shaking *alive* heat—it wraps around my face like a mask. It's bigger than me. Whatever it is.

There's a horrible sound; a wet, scraping moan. It's a real mess, limbs all around. I can't tell which way up it is, only stare at the huge, open mouth of gore, rib-teeth bared. Something shifts near my knee and I cry out, forgetting for a minute the danger of someone hearing me out here. I look between my knees and realize the dark brown shape that I thought was normal leaves is its head. Its eyes are still open, looking straight into me, knocking on my mind.

It makes another noise, a series of cavernous clicks, like its own belly balloon is crumpling and releasing its air, and I moan along with it. *I want to help you.* I reach for its face, forgetting every sane thing about parasites and contagion, but before it can wait for me, it's shivering and then just like that it's dead.

I sit with it.

And then I'm off and running.

I obviously don't mention it to anyone. The (Boy)s will want to do something with it, woodsmeat for free lying out there like that, but I want to keep it a secret. It's not for our world; it's for theirs. No one asks me though; too busy snarling around timed light about the migrants seeping into the Outskirts. Blaming them for the everything-mess. It's not their fault; just that their dustbowl cracked and now they've come to ours. We dustbowled them first. But (Boy) finds history boring and goes for me when I try and bring it up. "What would you know?" he rushes. "You didn't even go to school." I dodge his heavy-footedness and make for the outside. *Still enough sense to know you can't fight balloons.* They'll just keep bouncing out of the way, pulling us higher into the thin, ash air.

I don't usually venture outside during the afternoon, but if the air con's not paid, what difference does it make. I kick my way through the crispy twirls of dead wheat in our plot—if you put enough force into it, you can make the whole thing disappear into a swirling cloud of dust. Go up high enough and that's the grow-plots of the whole Outskirts; a ring of shrinking tendrils.

I head to the woods for shade, although the water still clinging inside the big trees spits out a nasty humidity that the bugs just love. They're the only flying things left, and not the ones we need. (Boy) keeps joking if none are spared from the sun, I'll have to get into one of those humiliating suits, a cotton bud of bug sperm in each hand, and waffle around like some giant joke-bee. It won't help, I try and tell him. They've all left already. No one in the City is waiting on joke crops anymore.

I'm thinking of ways to talk some sense into (Boy) when I come across the dead thing again. I can't believe it's slipped my mind already, but my gasp takes in a large mouthful of stench and then I'm coughing and gagging, doubled-over. I pull myself together and get a better look in the golden underwater-dapple of the woods. How can light still be beautiful, after all it has done?

The beast seems bigger in the daylight, puffed up. The wound is as wide as its body, a deep black-red, the blood dried thick around the edges. It looks like magma after the eruption is over, cooling in ribbed sludges around the base. I peer inside; there's about fifty billion maggots in there. I should pull away, but the sheer number keeps me glued in place, the noise of them; there's so many. Enough. All together. I circle around to find the face I tried to hold; its eyes are still open, but the maggots are in there too. So fast. No time for mourning out here.

I sit with it, watching the maggots at work, their movement hypnotizing. The smell is rock-hard, but once it has wormed its way through me, I no longer notice it. There's something leaking from the mouth; its last words. What were they? *Well that fucking hurts*, probably. Where has this thing been hiding? It must've been a smart one, although it has been a long time since these woods stopped being for 'A Stroll on a Sunday' and 'the Nation's well-being'; the lone dark mass left alone in the surrounding unfurl of farmland.

Still. It lived undisturbed long enough to grow big. Old enough to have moved all around these dead hills, to have found food enough to stay moving. Old enough to have had babies? Were there others? What had killed it, mauled it like this? Taken a chunk out of it like an apple? I sit with it until night, feeling bruised and broken along with it until I can hear the danger. Then I hurry home. The sun is red-raw from screaming.

I make sure to keep the beast in my head all night, holding its image there as vigil while the rage pumps through the house. I wriggle out again at first light: I want to see if the maggots are early risers, lining up to clock-in; if they sleep on the job; if they sleep at all. But when I get into the woods to the spot, there is a crowd of different beasts standing around it, smaller than the dead one and more wolfish, and above them like a crown, a swooping circle of many-coloured birds and I crouch back and watch because I've never been one for the predators, but then I wake up tucked up in the creases of a tall, black tree and I'm not sure if I've dreamt the whole thing. I have moss in my nose and I finger-close one nostril and hook it out like you did when you were a kid, before going over to my dead friend, and it's just the maggots left, wax-white and grinning. As I watch them, I feel them bubbling through my own brain, writhing like (Boy) and the belly balloons and the dead wheat and the rest of it, and I rip off my clothes and lie down as close as I dare and hope I will be eaten away as well.

I go home when the fires are ringing around the hills and we've gotta declare. Admit defeat. I don't fancy being there for (Boy)'s speech but someone's gotta be the voice of reason. I'll come back as soon as I can.

It's only the next morning, but last night had so much crammed into it I feel thousands of years older, with none of the alleged wisdom. Or none of the alleged respect. I tried to tell them, but no one would listen. They think all our problems are coming from inside, from the City; (Boy) wants to go in, take something back. "It's empty," I said, but no one would listen. I leave it to them—fuck 'em—and bring something to eat alongside the maggots and the worms. I look down at my meat-paste sandwich, then over at the beast. How are maggots eating better than me? Is that fair? But then again, why not? I wonder how they found it, out here in the nothing? It means they've also been out there as well, hiding. I look around at the trees and ground. I count two things, but there must be a million, easy, a million things and beings and brains all worming their way along, no thoughts or cares for our troubles back at the housing. I look down at my sandwich and concentrate on splitting myself and eating it from all sides at once, from the outside in, consuming it. Becoming it.

When (Boy) finally finds me, I am more sandwich than woman

and he tells me this is unacceptable.

(Boy) sits in the hot-dark kitchen with me, me drinking a warm Dr Pepper cos there's no good water left. He clears his throat and says he's called Waste Control about the animal, that they will come to remove it before bigger animals come and cause more trouble for the rebels out in the woods, and even though I know he's lying and he's planning on taking up the meat and getting what he can for it, I smile sugary-down because that means the predators were real, there are others and they already know where to find the beast. It means the woods are not just one thing. Not ours either.

"They'll never find it," I say, but he says, "Oh, but I'll lead them there," and I say, "No, you won't," and then I am maggots.

And then he is there, across my back, and I am bringing them dinner.

Now I get to see it from the start again, but they don't jump right in. They leave him well alone at first, letting him cook and swell in the heat for a couple of days, as if to make sure he's really gone. Maybe there is a mourning period out here after all. Things are worse than ever back at the housing. I'm worried at first someone will go looking for (Boy), but then the late summer smog meets the fire-ash and no one can see. In fact, it makes people blind. When it lifts, there'll be fifty other (Boy)s to fill his place of one, and all of them will be making speeches.

I'm better out here with my Blowflies: we got one brief flash of connection last night as it sloughed off the City, and I found their name. Our name. I'm so stupid; I imagined them crawling across the nothing until they found the beast, but they come as flies, leaving their eggs in the Active Decay stage to blossom into the heady festival I know and love today. They are making some real progress now; like so full the body is moving again, like it will jump up and canter off, and I think about cantering and the leaves and the larvae and the birds and the wind.

Autumn comes, dragged, bruised and shaking by its hot-headed sister, who dumps her in the woods, and there she weeps brown all over everything, but better than the smokey-barbecue of the other ridges. I come out to escape the screaming and the news channels and the gang violence over the food. The (Boy)s are out of ideas. No imports now. All our own brown for ourselves. Yummy.

Leaves cover the bodies and the ground starts drinking them in.

When I arrive, I panic because I can't see them, but then I un-cover the stern fungi growing through them and I sit back and try to listen instead, closing my eyes and opening them and the shoots are already up, growing through the ribcage and it makes me feel funny; hot like I haven't felt in a long time—hot like I can't remember when or how. I want them to grow through me, and I take off my jeans and split myself down the middle, maggot-style, pushing me down onto the earth and the earth up into me, and I giggle at first when they start to grow but then I stop giggling and throw my head back and my screams become birdsong.

The housing is burnt now. The rest have become migrants themselves. I'd like to have seen (Boy)'s face. I watch them from the edge of the woods, trailing away with bunched faces and fists across the lit backdrop like figures from hell. I don't know if they listened to the speeches in the end. I count them off as they disappear over the horizon. One, one, one.

The beast is almost part of everything else again, and I remove (Boy)'s clothes to help make everyone more comfortable. I sit with them while the fires burn, and then the floods rise, and then the fighting fights, and then the blah blah and the blah blah. I've stopped listening to that world now. This is my home—if I'm allowed to stay.

Bugs live in my hair now. At some point, the bigger creatures return and snack around me. They eat the brown mushrooms, avoid the flush reds and the mustard yellows. I follow suit. I think about the fungus eating the dead and then me eating the fungus. Am I the living dead? Is everything?

Winter comes, and I curl up to the heat factory and try to sleep. Outside the woods, it is louder for longer, but in here it is quiet. They must have forgotten about us. I dream of being sucked down into the soil and separated into my useful parts, some of me going to this and some to that and it's all happening at once, in many different bubbles, and some of me becomes earth and then smaller bits and then just elements and atoms and then just ideas, swapped around in drunken trades among the nitrates and the carbons. But then another part of me is pushed upward, out into the air again as swollen fruits, and it feels like I'm trying to hold something in that's really funny and then I can't hold it in and I am spat up as spores, out in a little hot laughing puff into the freezing ultradark. Those parts of me float through the woods, past where the beast once lay. I'm almost sad that I can't even see its body now, but it's not really gone, it's right here with me, laughing with me at the hilarious joke that is new life, coming again, trying again, and together we are carried past all the millions and millions that I can now see, and then higher up, above the treeline, out into the world—and we see there are plenty of opportunities for landing and growth.

Zachary Keesey

Two Minutes Until the Bell

Nonfiction

I met Alaska thirty seconds after entering the room. The students shuffled in as I stood at the front of the class, dropping my substitute teacher bag on the frayed, black swivel chair behind the desk. Alaska ran up to me with a friend in tow and a big, beaming smile.

"Hi!" they said, barely containing their excitement. "Are you the sub this afternoon?"

I straightened my shirt as I turned to face them. "Yes, I am," I said, flipping on my substitute teacher mode a little earlier than anticipated. "I'm Mr. Keesey. What are your names?"

The friend spoke first. "I'm Desiree, and this is Alaska." Alaska waved.

We exchanged pleasantries. I was surprised, as most middle schoolers didn't usually want to talk to subs. Some did, but it was rare. I was always happy to make connections with students, however, so I was ready to ask them my usual 'get-to-know-you' questions. Before I could, though, Alaska jumped in.

"I want you to know that my name isn't on the roster."

"Oh, it's not?" I asked, a little shaken by the abruptness of the statement. "What is it under?" I pulled out the attendance sheet from my bag and held it in front of Alaska, who scanned the paper and placed a finger on a name three-quarters of the way down the sheet.

"That's my birth name, but it's not what I go by."

It's not uncommon for students to try and get you to call them something other than the name on the roster. I'm not talking about saying 'Dave' instead of 'David' or 'Abi' instead of 'Abigail', though. Those students typically don't care. It's the students who, during roll call, will yell out, "Actually, I go by 'El Fuego Terrible'," when you call for 'Michael'. After you substitute teach for a while, you get a sense for when kids are trying to mess with you.

Alaska was not one of those.

"Instead, can you please call me 'Alaska'? Also, I prefer they/them pronouns."

"Okay," I said with a nod, assuming that would be the end of it and that I could get ready for the upcoming period. The bell would be ringing soon. However, Alaska must have misinterpreted my tone to be one of skepticism rather than acceptance, and they started rambling.

"I promise I'm not lying, and I'm not trying to trick you or anything, it's just that I don't really think of myself as a girl or a boy. I'm really more in-between and neither, I guess, and I just—"

As Alaska spoke, clearly a bit flustered, I noticed Desiree standing steadfastly beside her friend, eyes darting between Alaska and me.

"So," I interjected, "would you say you identify as gender non-binary or gender non-conforming, then?"

Alaska's and Desiree's mouths dropped open. "You know the words?" Alaska asked.

"I am familiar with them. I'm not an expert or anything, but yeah."

Alaska's eyes widened. They bounced up and down. "I can't believe you know those words! Almost none of the teachers here know them, and hardly any of the students."

"Do you have this conversation with teachers a lot?" I asked.

"Not so much anymore. Most of them get it now that the year is almost over, but they still make mistakes and occasionally call me by my birth name, or they use the wrong pronouns."

"And subs?"

"No, never! They always think I'm lying or just refuse to call me Alaska."

Desiree nodded along as Alaska spoke.

"It must be difficult to have this conversation with every sub you meet, only to get rejected every time."

Alaska's gaze fell from mine, settling on the whiteboard behind me, as if lost in thought.

"But hey," I said, "you have Desiree here to support you, right? Not everybody has an ally who will come up with them to meet a total stranger." Desiree beamed at the compliment.

Alaska looked over at Desiree. "She is a good friend, and several of the other kids in the class are supportive, too. Not all of them, but some are. And it's also important that I do this, because if I don't educate people, who will?"

I thanked Alaska for sharing her story with me, but now, with under a minute to go until the bell rang, I needed them to take their seats so I could finish getting ready. They hurried to their spots, and as I skimmed the lesson plan, I overheard Alaska excitedly talking to their friends about our conversation.

I didn't get a chance to see Alaska again after that; the school district I worked for was large, and getting called for the same class more than once was unlikely. But I hope that Alaska is still asking, still speaking out as new adults enter the room.

And if they refuse to listen, I hope Alaska remains undeterred for the next one.

Sindhu Rajasekaran

காகம் | Crow

Urban autumn, leaves turn colour
Beneath tall glass towers
A concrete visage. An empty mind.
I stand in this faraway land
Under a stoplight.
Above me, a black crow
Its shrill caw pierces through cold air,
Look in its knowing eye

Memories from another time;
My Amma's gruff old voice:
நம் முன்னோர்கள் காகங்களாக வருவாங்க
our ancestors' spirits will visit us as crows

Superstition or sign—light turns green
Charcoal wings take flight
I walk to the other side, mystified
Is it my Amma come to see me,
Or have delusions taken hold, again

A little war ensues
between my mind and tongue—
They speak different languages.
The empire's legacy.

Silence and alliance.

I sit under a dreamy tree,
Take heed I live on unceded land;
The crow and raven are symbolic
To the First Nations people.
Ancient wisdom entices me
To remember and feel
The soggy bark, timeworn, wrinkled
Like my Amma's skin
The day before she died.

All the distance fades away
The lance of memory
Pricks and punctures—
She never wanted me to leave

In Tamil, காகம், the crow,
Is a shadowy creature
Surreptitious. Divulging
Truths between eons.
Here, its cousin the raven has many names
In native myths, for the Skwxwú7mesh Úxwumixw
Whose land now I call home
The black-winged one is a trickster
Catalyst for change:
Teaching us the ways of the world
Neither good nor bad.

Glass reflects the shifty indigo sky.
The sun will soon set.
Raw wounds will stand exposed
Dilemmas manifold
Belonging. Unbelonging.
Everyday stresses of monies
Ambitions, its lack and slack
The purpose of existence.
I'm so jaded, there's no truth

I look up to the tree.
My mind spread out

As barren branches
Seeking ~
But what?

Amma never approved
Of vacillation. She always knew.
Told me: watch your back
The world owes you no favours

A moment later
Icy drops of rain fall
The airy spirits of glade
Enter cityspace
And I know: அவள் வந்தாள்;
She came.

Tal Bressette
Grandmothers Lament

Content warning: violence

Tina and Colten
I see your beautiful
smiling brown faces
You look like
My grandchildren
I remember you
I honour you
I stand for you

O Canada
Your plausible deniability
Is no longer defensible
While our children
are murdered
with no consequence for
Your silence
Your collusion
Your consent

Our children
Collateral Damage
in this poverty war

This endless war
upon our lands
our way of life
gutted and sacrificed
in the name
of Corporate Greed

We bury our dead
filled with cancers
our young people
filled with drugs and alcohol
while our children
wait and watch and learn
Some run
some get caught
some get shot
some get thrown away
into rivers and along highways
like garbage

O Canada
your home and native land
that land you visit every summer
at your cottage by the lake
in the crossover that you drive
from that city where you live
insulated from the truth

the truth
about us
about you
about Canada

You read the morning news
Sanitized for your consumption
on your phone on the subway
from your glass and concrete towers
You see photos of First Nation families
sad and sick and dying
and you think:

They get everything for free
Why can't they just get a job
Why can't they just get over it
Why can't they just be like us

O Canada
Your true north strong and free
But you never see the war
being fought on your own land
Just another pipeline stand-off
Just another barricade
Just another bunch of Lazy Indians
With nothing else to do
Nothing left to lose

Your Duty to Consult
A flyer in the mail
an information session
A give-away for corporate swag
A report that says:
No one lives here except a few broken Indians
Offer them jobs
Offer them a share
Offer them schools
homes
drinking water

Keep them on their reserves
Keep the opiates flowing
Give them enough to shut them up
Give them more to shut them down
Give them another government program
Enough to start but not enough to go around

Get them off the god-damned land
So we can drill another hole
Strip another mountain
Poison another lake
Clearcut old growth forests
Prop up the GDP

These Indians don't know what they've got
Give them enough rope
They'll hang themselves

Keep them in their rural ghettos
where we don't have to see them
or think about them
or wonder what it's like to be them

And the Grandmothers Lament
and Hope and Pray
and hold on to their young
until they break away

Some run
Some get caught
Some get shot
Some get thrown away
into rivers and along highways
like garbage

No Justice for Tina and Colten
No Peace O Canada

Sonali Misra
Sway with Me

Content warning: drug abuse

Samaira squinted at the hunched-up form of her husband Rishaan on the hotel bed, but it didn't afford her any fresh insight into the scene laid out before her. A soft snore floated from his direction and, in tandem, a perturbed sigh escaped her mouth. If it weren't for this sign of faint dissent and her constantly tapping right foot, one would assume she were at peace.

She wasn't sure whether his unconsciousness stemmed from exhaustion at running amok in Goa all night, or if he'd simply passed out from the myriad of alcohol that had entered his body, along with variously coloured pills. His shoulder-length kohl hair fanned out as he lay on his side, the position Samaira had forced him into so he wouldn't choke if he had to spew again. She hadn't managed to wipe off the vomit crusted on his chin yet. His arm dangled next to the bucket she'd placed by the bed, along with a bottle of water.

She shifted her weight on the brown faux-leather couch and heard the crackling of tiny objects that had crept into the gaps between the cushions and frame. Her childlike curiosity would've usually made her lift the cushions and examine the items just as an archaeologist would study relics of a long-lost civilization. But no, not this time. Right then, her mind was swirling in an ocean of doubts and despair. Her muscles twitched, ever so slightly, as though her heart was trying to kick-start itself in a drowning body.

Rishaan's face appeared before her eyes—radiant and lovely, beseeching and sincere—nothing like the one belonging to the being in the bed: drained of colour, more at home on the screen of a black-and-white film. *"Please, Samaira, we have to try. We have to try to save us, the us we used to be. Help me save us, Samaira. Please."* His voice had broken on the last word as he'd laid his hand on her shoulder and looked into her eyes with the love that had been so familiar to her for eight years. Eight years. Until it had smogged over two years ago, much like the brightness of his eyes. She had vowed her marriage would be different from the one she'd witnessed growing up, and it was—no raised voices or hands—but the sickness took the form of another beast. And last night, it had taken over the man she had hoped to embrace once again.

Those fucking pills. When they'd reappeared in Rishaan's hand after he'd promised—he'd *sworn*—he was done with them, that was when Samaira had taken off from the seedy nightclub he'd dragged her to the previous night. This wasn't what their second honeymoon was supposed to be; it was meant to breathe life into their marriage. She should've known it was already a carcass that no amount of kicking would make alive once more.

A flush resounded in the deadened silence of the room, followed by a stranger's sloppy footsteps from the toilet. The interloper rubbed her left eye with the end of her shirtsleeve, which was too long for her scraggy frame. She shuffled past the lump Rishaan formed on the bed and the figure Samaira effected on the sofa—with her legs spread apart, back stooped, elbows resting on her thighs and hands forming a triangle at the gap's centre, Rodin would've proudly labelled her 'The Worrier'. Neither a word nor a look was exchanged. The stranger continued her dragging motion until she reached the mattress on the floor. Upon reaching their destination, her limbs folded into themselves as her body slumped over next to a slumbering man. Samaira didn't know his name either, since Rishaan was slurring by the time he'd brought the pair to their room six hours ago, around noon.

Perhaps the energy transferred in that moment—the final push that Samaira's humming body needed came from the loss of tension in the woman's frame. Samaira jumped to her feet and, in four long strides, reached the door. She averted her eyes from Rishaan. She wouldn't, *couldn't*, look at him anymore. Nor did she glance back as she heard the lock click into place, shutting the door on putrid claustrophobia. The air was thin in the corridor too, so she walked on the musty carpet toward the elevator. Not having enough patience for the red lights to flicker the number of her floor, she turned to the emergency exit and scurried down three flights of stairs, jumping from the fourth-to-last step and flailing her arms to regain her balance.

She stepped on the scratched tiles of the hotel lobby and darted for the main door, ignoring the pointed disinterest of the concierge who preferred to save his fawning for smartly dressed guests who knew better than to be publicly seen in the crumpled T-shirt and jeans that clothed Samaira's lanky figure, or at the very least had the decency to be foreigners carrying unfamiliarly coloured bills. Samaira didn't have the time to harangue him for being racist against his own kind. No, her mind was focused on one task: she needed to find Diya.

The evening sun glinted through the interlaced beams above the pick-up/drop-off point, their spiderweb shadow encasing Samaira within. And she stood there, stumped. This wasn't how it usually worked. Back home in Delhi, her feet would locate Diya, even when her head didn't know how. In Goa—the not-entirely Unknown after her four-day stay, but still the Unfamiliar—Samaira's feet quivered with doubt. Hesitation trembled through her ankle to her toes as her right foot raised itself, took a step and then backtracked, not entirely sure of its role in all this.

A warmth spread over the nape of her neck as she recalled the last time she had seen Diya. Her hair had seemed afire under the glare of the alley light in Delhi. *"Goa? Oh, I'd love it there! I've always been fascinated by those rocky beaches—have you felt it? That sense of alone-ness, which detaches you from the world, yet connects you to it? I see myself there. I see us there."*

Of course. Her feet turned westward, toward the sea.

The wind was uncharacteristically strong for October. Though Samaira only half-noticed it, as well as her surroundings as they changed from posher pockets to hubbubs of the local markets, from long shiny sedans to rikshaws, from shutter-clicks of tourists' cameras to the pealing laughter of street urchins. She bent her head low and stuck her hands in her jean pockets, where the right one found her cell phone. She unmindfully drummed her fingers on it, and then let it go. She didn't need to call Rishaan ... anyway, everything would be alright in some time. She was going to be alright.

As she stood waiting for the traffic light to flash a green for pedestrians, she recalled the first time she'd landed upon the place in Delhi all those years ago. It had taken her by surprise, but it was exactly what she'd needed. What she still did need. She never told anyone about it, not even her parents. They wouldn't understand.

Green light.

She stumbled on the chipped sidewalk but regained control before she could fall. She mumbled an 'excuse me, I'm sorry' to no one in particular. Maybe it was customary. Or perhaps she'd simply aimed it at the world.

It was near; she could feel the ends of her body—her toes, fingers and head—buzz with expectation. Her sluggish step switched to a trot that soon became a sprint, until her lungs gasped with protest. Her feet suddenly came to a halt. She'd reached, and just in time.

Dusk glowed over the sand blanketing the skeleton of rocks underneath, their joints protruding in a jagged charcoal-greyness. With every high current crashing against the shore, she felt a wave of peace wash over her. She looked around but saw no one. Panic threatened to rise, but she regulated her breathing, clutching on to hope, no, her *faith* in Diya. She wouldn't let Samaira down, not her Diya. The sun dipped below the horizon, and her world was cast in a harmonious black.

"I knew you'd come."

The voice, smooth as a weathered pebble, flowed all around her. But habit told her it came from behind. She smiled.

"I couldn't stay away," Samaira said, turning around.

Diya flashed Samaira a grin that dazzled brighter than any star in the night sky and lit up her hazel eyes. She took a few steps in Samaira's direction, the train of her white lace dress sweeping behind, and shifted to Samaira's left to circle around her. Diya leaned in and whispered, "You know what you have to do."

Samaira looked at the coarse sand and even coarser stones, at the angry waves and then finally at Diya's face that held just a hint of a side smile, as always. Samaira closed her eyes and counted to ten.

3 … She wondered if it'd be the same.

7 … Surely, it would be.

9 … It *had* to be.

Her eyelids lifted to flashes of colour all around, brightened by tiki lamps thrust into the soft sand. The world's muddled tint had finally been shorn off. Her ears popped open, and Diya's sparkling laugh entered them like a caress. Samaira beamed and strode ahead, Diya following her lead. Samaira zigzagged her way around the building blocks, colouring books, balls and stuffed toys peeking out of the golden sand. A jazz band played in their motley costumes on her left under orange-and-magenta beach umbrellas, and moonlight glinted off the now-calm waves that swayed along with the movement of the strings. All her friends paused from their dancing circle to hail her with a loud cheer. She waved back with a grin so wide it hurt her cheeks. She heard a boisterous laugh and wasn't surprised when the owner of that voice exclaimed, "Oh, lookie who's found her way here! Didn't I tell you, darling? That girl loves us, she damn well can't stay away. Ah, empty threats, the whole lot of them!" Bernard stood with his wife Clara, daring Samaira to refute. She shook her head as a bubble of laughter escaped her throat. She welcomed the hug she knew was coming.

"My dear girl, you know you're always cherished here, don't you?"

"Yes, of course, Bernard," Samaira replied while taking a few steps to the right to make way for the cartwheeling acrobats in glossy red leotards. Clara pulled Bernard toward that group, forcing him to tip his top hat in way of bidding farewell for the moment.

Diya hadn't left Samaira's side all this time. She asked Diya for a dance. A sly smile appeared on her face as she sassed back, "It's about time."

The music changed from a quick, lively jig to a slow, blissful sway. Samaira pulled Diya in, who wrapped her arms around Samaira's neck. Their bodies moved in time with the tune. Diya's fiery red hair framed her face, and a lock threatened to creep over one eye. She rested her head on Samaira's shoulder, who took in the scene around her with a tranquil sigh. The lush palm trees reached out to encircle the dancers underneath in an effort to protect them from the cruel world outside. One of the elephants of the band suddenly sneezed but managed not to miss a beat on the double bass. Bernard's squiggly pink tail rebelled against being suffocated in his tuxedo pants and snuck out as he brushed Clara's mane from her face, who neighed affectionately in his embrace. The others left their laughter-tinged conversations midway to join the dance and exist in the moment, in the song, in the sway.

The phone buzzed in Samaira's pocket, and the music stopped. Diya stiffened in Samaira's arms but didn't lift her head. The dreaded monophonic tone rang out, and the colours around Samaira dulled a shade. Diya raised her eyes, her hair a sombre auburn, and reassured Samaira with a smile. It rang again. She let Diya go and reached for her phone.

"Samaira? Are you there?" Rishaan's voice broke in.

She just about managed to mumble, "Yes."

"I'm sorry for last night. I slipped up … but it won't happen again, I promise. I love you, Samaira. I need you. Please come back?"

She looked about and found everyone arrested in their movements, their eyes fixed on her, awaiting her response with a united bated breath.

Diya leaned closer, her breath warm and comforting on Samaira's face, and whispered, "We will *always* be here for you. Whenever you need us."

She kissed Samaira's cheek and retreated a step. Samaira closed her eyes for a moment and focused, ensuring she remembered that feeling, that image.

"Samaira?" Rishaan's voice quivered.

"Yes. I'm coming back to you, Rishaan."

She reopened her eyes, alone, in her sepia world.

Pamela Medland
Deluge

On the fortieth day we woke to
flotsam wriggling above the tideline.

On the forty-first day starfish crept up the boat launch,
splayed on sidewalks, glistened on dark asphalt.

On the forty-second day mussels crested the seawall.
Rain-soaked joggers slogged through a black soup
of crushed crustaceans.

On the forty-third day octopi crawled through the drains,
long tentacles explored sewers and all our secret places.

On the forty-fourth day a sea lion lumbered up Granville,
shoved through a crowd of gawking shoppers,
shook gobs of sea foam from his whiskers.

On the forty-fifth day the sky lightened,
shore crabs scuttled up sand,
staggered down Hastings in a gentle rain.

On the forty-sixth day the sun broke through,
houses and storefronts hung out fresh hues.

Pale, we crept from our havens,
wore the crusts of our psyches like shells.

Marina Stepanova
Sunrise on a Double-sunned Earth

Would it be sci-fi to name the sun a double star
More troubling as a nuclear device
Blaring into a subway run by giant rats
Bio-engineered into servile engines?

And a war where I imagine our war veterans
Will outnumber the conscientious objectors.
(Under a more favourable sky
Beyond the ocean still an ocean
Demonstrations led by proxy servos

Mostly charred but very much alive
Circuits still run wet and never stall
They promise democratic replacement
Something that will come some day

Across the ocean.) Here we are all
Manufacture. Of the force that stoves
Factories and power plants
Grown into what we have long called trademark

National goods free-traded into genetic
Tradition. A tomato I share with my
Fellow passenger makes him sing in Spanish

But it doesn't last long as our car implodes
From the front. We have to trudge the rest
Of the way, corpses as baggage. Our train
Doesn't worship at the station. Something

I forgot as I dreamed the sun. The rains come down
Upon us in our march. Stragglers are consumed
Where they lie. There is still a nature to
Contend with as we winded arrive at the front.

Double star contend with us. The enemy
Pierced with suctioning devices they fly equipped
Over us in squadrons. But it is when they land
That they are deadly. Now we admire

Their ingenious arrays of death. Fangs
Out and wetted. Take the breath away.
Our God allows. Their fragrant tombs.
Into the double day when we end the killing by killing again.

Lexie Angelo

The Beast of the Two-lettered Place

I heard them talking about the two-lettered place again. Everyone at the office was either going there, or just coming back. There are other places to go, but no one mentions them. I am curious about the two-lettered place, but I've been too afraid to go. My coworkers insist I will love it, but then they tell me about the beasts; the ones who attack the town and eat garbage. "It's not a big deal," they say, reminiscing about the beasts. "I saw one by the highway, but some idiot ruined it for me because he got out of his car to take a picture."

I didn't understand because I, too, would want a photo of the beast. But it is not allowed. "You will die," they tell me. "It will rip your face off."

So, like I said, I haven't made any plans to go.

Instead, I try to fit in with the locals here, in my city. But I can never get it right. They know I don't belong, even though I look just like them. I take the train to work in the morning, but every day, I am late. I arrive at nine, and I am late. I arrive at eight-thirty, and I am still late. I've heard whispers of people who arrive at six, but that must be a rumour meant to scare me just like the beasts in the two-lettered place. At four o'clock in the afternoon, I loosen my tie, look up from my desk and most people are gone. Some stay later, but the cleaners are already vacuuming by then. They hoover under my feet and empty my recycling bin with a look of confusion. They don't like it when I am still here. They smile, but not because they are happy. To them, I am like a lamp or a chair. Something to vacuum around.

In the evenings, I walk home to my apartment, which is sometimes called a condo. I thought condos were covered in glass, but that turned out not to be true, and my coworkers laughed at me when I said it. Yet any time we pass a new construction site, they ask, "Who *actually* wants to live in these condos?" And the design is right there on a sign: a watercolour painting of a towering glass structure.

My apartment, or condo, is not glass. It is concrete with half-moon balconies overlooking a pair of garbage dumpsters. The building faces a long stretch of bars, restaurants and cannabis stores with names like Sweet Tree and Spirit Leaf. I walk past them and peer in the windows. One night, I opened the door expecting something exotic, but there was only a bored woman standing in front of IKEA shelves. She asked me if I collected points and I wondered what the points were for, but I was too embarrassed to ask.

It is difficult to eat or drink alone in my city, so on my walk home, I order take-out and eat in front of my television. I tried going out for a drink once, at a place where other people were also drinking, but the server was confused. He didn't understand I only wanted to drink. He sat me at a large booth because *it's quiet tonight* and my friends could join me later. But nobody joined me later. And after the third time he encouraged me to order half-priced chicken wings, I left.

There is so much pressure to eat food, expecially outdoors. Along the sidewalks, tables are bordered by low fences designed to keep patrons contained. There are long queues to get inside the fence where the drinks overflow, music blares and smokers are ordered to stand on the other side. The smoke wafts over the heads of the other drinkers, but if you smoke anywhere else, people get angry. I smoke on my balcony now. It is the only space where I can be sure I will not upset anyone.

Mina started at my office on Monday morning. When my supervisor introduced her, we discovered we had the same last name. She was assigned a cubicle across the hall, so now when I lean back in my chair, I can see wisps of her hair trailing down her back. She's wearing a cream-coloured blouse with little strawberry-jewelled buttons that twinkle. My supervisor spent the morning ushering her to meetings while staring absently into his phone. I watched her as she stood patiently, greeting each strange new face. She held a small notebook in front of her navy skirt that cut across her legs like nightfall. Her calves looked smooth like carved cedar, her ankles like river pebbles softened by a millennium of arctic water.

"I am Mina," she said an hour later as we stood together in the photocopying room. She was searching for a box of tissues.

"I remember, you came by my desk earlier," I said. She blushed and apologized for not recalling my face. I didn't mind. I handed her a box of tissues from a cabinet marked *Do not open*.

"That is strange," she remarked at the cabinet that was easily opened. I clicked its black door shut.

"You can take from the cabinet, so long as nothing appears to be disturbed. It is refilled on the fifteenth of the month."

"And you're sure I can take from it?" Mina asked, holding the box of tissues to her chest.

"Only when you are alone," I paused. "Or with me."

Mina smiled and turned down the corridor toward her desk, clutching her prize tightly. I watched her pebbles alternate in unison. Her hair swept her shoulders like a raven's feather. And I knew then I was in love.

I sat at my desk for two weeks, nervously typing and twitching. I pushed my chair back every few hours and watched the colours of the flowers change. Buttercup on Thursday. Marigold on Monday. Rose on Tuesday. Sometimes it was dresses, other days sharp grey slacks that hid the stones that made my palms tingle. On Monday morning, I opened an email from the CEO inviting all employees to a fancy breakfast function that served alcohol and pancakes. The breakfast was on the upcoming Friday, and we were gifted the day off. Everyone in the office whooped. Mina asked me about the invitation while we chatted by the forbidden cabinet. I unlocked the door and she selected a pink highlighter. I took some binder clips.

"I've never heard of a drunken breakfast before," she said quietly.

"It's a ten-day celebration for CEOs who like to eat carbs, I think."

Mina bit her bottom lip. I was transfixed by the perfection of the curvature, the tinted curl of her expression. It looked like she wanted to ask me something.

"I can answer more questions if you have them," I said while stuffing my hands in my pockets. The printer whirred to life and began spitting out a stack of sheets. Mina flipped through the pages and didn't look up when she spoke.

"What do you know about the two-lettered place?" she whispered. The printer made mechanical crunching sounds. Someone must have sent a staple job.

"We can't talk about it here," I said, darting my eyes to the open door.

"What do you mean?" Mina asked. "It's all I hear about. I need to know."

"I could get in trouble," I said. A lump formed in my throat.

"I want to go," she said, turning with the documents in her hand. "I want you to take me."

There was a cough in the hallway, and she vanished from the room. I quickly shut the cabinet door just before a tall man with a wrinkled suit turned the corner.

"You have to sign those items out, son."

I nodded, pretending to understand.

"I bet you're excited for the breakfast."

I nodded again. "Of course. Yes."

"Don't forget your buckle and hat. You want to look the part."

I gulped with fear.

Buckle.

Hat.

What could this mean? I had to warn Mina.

I debated my options but eventually settled on writing Mina an email. I spent all afternoon editing each word and changing the phrases around. I even missed an important meeting because I was so consumed with getting my thoughts just right. I didn't know the rules for inviting a coworker to my apartment alone. What if we left the office together and the cleaners noticed? Could they be trusted to keep my secret?

When I clicked send, I let out an exhale. The reply came instantly.

"Yes."

For the first time, I decided to leave before the cleaners arrived. Mina waited at a bubble tea shop until I texted her that it was safe to come over. She would take the route past the Spirit Leaf, the ramen bar and the restaurant with a metal cleaver for a name. She appeared in my lobby carrying a lavender cardigan and a purse in the shape of a cupcake. Her hair smelled of sweet cherry, and it tugged at me as I led her inside my apartment and brought her a glass of water. She sat on my favourite chair with her ankles crossed. I sat opposite her, on a hard sofa I bought online. The pictures made it look comfortable, but it was really a rock. Eleven reviewers gave it five stars.

"Did anyone see you leave?" I asked.

"Only the cleaner with the yellow frock. But she smiled at me."

"They will stop smiling eventually. The smiles are bad."

"Why are they bad?"

"I think they prefer to clean with no one watching."

"I thought the smile was nice," she said, turning her gaze out the picture window. Outside, a bird with a black body and white wing-tips shrieked at us. In the distance, the shriek was answered, and the bird flew away.

"I like it here. You live with the birds," she said, tucking her feather-hair behind her ears.

"Oh, them? They are not well liked," I replied. "We have that in common, I guess."

"I like you," Mina said, reaching for her glass of water.

My voice suddenly felt like wet cotton sheets. I wanted to sit next to Mina, but I was rooted to my rock. My legs refused to move.

"I bet the birds travel to the two-lettered place," she said finally. "I'm sure of it."

"Of course they do, but they have nothing to fear. They live in the sky."

"What is there to fear? Everyone says they love it."

"Didn't they tell you about the beasts?"

"Wait—no."

"That's why I can't take you. I wanted to tell you here, in private."

Mina looked down at the carpet that I should have vacuumed. The crumbs from a week's worth of dinners looked up at her.

"Will they attack us?" she asked.

"They might."

"What do the beasts look like?"

"Some are black, others are brown. They have slick-wet fangs and spiked fur. They swat at foreigners and eat garbage from the town."

"But why does everyone love it there? I don't understand."

"I guess they are not afraid of the beasts."

"Then we shouldn't be either," Mina said. She stood up abruptly and crossed the room, dropping down next to me on the rock. My heart thrummed in my chest, and my cheeks went red.

Mina took my hand. Her brown eyes locked with mine.

Suddenly I found myself in a different place entirely. My living room was no longer a world I recognized; the edges warped and blurred. My throat felt sticky hot. The rock became gravity itself, pulling me down underneath an ocean. Mina was asking me something, so I nodded.

"So, you will take me?"

The room wobbled into focus. I gasped for air.

"Where? When?"

"The two-lettered place, silly. You are brave. That's why your name means protector."

My inhale sharpened my anxiety. Fear swirled in my chest like whorls of paint on a paper canvas. It felt like my insides were getting disconnected. Someone was unplugging my organs and reconnecting them in the wrong places. Spleen stitched with lung. Colon attached with brain. Heart linked with liver.

"Mina, I—"

"We will go on Friday," she said resolutely. Her knee knocked into mine.

My skin erupted. "But the breakfast—"

"They won't notice us missing. Everyone will be drunk."

My mind raced back to the man in the wrinkled suit. *Don't forget your buckle and hat.*

"Okay," I replied.

Mina's eyes widened and she leaned over and kissed me on the cheek.

"Pick me up at nine in the morning," she said, grabbing her cupcake purse from the table. She stood up to leave. "I'll text you my address."

Mina slipped out of my apartment, condo, universe; yet her cherry scent still lingered. I thought about ordering dinner, but all I could do was sit on my rock and stare at the shrieking birds until nightfall.

On Friday, I woke up at six in the morning. The sky was still purple-grey. I made coffee because I didn't know what else to do. Down on the street below, people were jogging. A woman in a suit waited at a bus stop while clutching a briefcase. Surely, this was still a dream. On the rock sofa, I had organized a rucksack of provisions for the trip to the two-lettered place. I packed granola bars with chocolate chips, two bottles of water and a change of clothes. I didn't know how far we would be driving, or if we would make it home that evening, so I included a toothbrush, deodorant and condom just in case. I didn't know what to bring for the beasts. I thought about a knife, but I didn't want to get that close. What did the creatures fear? Loud noises? I thought about the shrieking birds. They scattered every time someone clapped. Perhaps the beasts feared applause too.

An hour into the drive, Mina assured me no one in our office would notice our absence. "They hardly notice anything," she said, shifting in her lightweight jacket. She was dressed for hiking, and her bag was heavier than mine, but I didn't ask what she had packed.

"They notice when the internet goes down," I said while accelerating around a corner. The smooth highway was void of cars. Only the trees and mountains loomed ahead.

Mina nodded. "Emotions are the internet. They are the same thing."

"I don't know if I have emotions at work," I said. "I only have meetings."

"I have a strategy meeting every Thursday, but it isn't real. I go for a walk instead," she said, opening the glove compartment and shutting it again. I wished I had placed something interesting in there, something that would have impressed her.

"You could invite me to the strategy meeting."

"What would we discuss?" Mina asked, her eyebrows raised.

"Well, for starters, we could discuss what we're going to do when we get to the two-lettered place. Most people go camping in the woods."

"I've heard them talk about camping, but I'm not interested in the woods. I have heard of another place, a meadow in the sky."

"That doesn't sound real."

"I think it is. There is a sign."

We didn't speak much on the drive. The open road seemed to create a lightness in the vehicle, and the silence didn't feel like wet cotton anymore. It felt like a warm breeze, or a peach tea. I thought about the meadow in the sky. I pictured Mina laying in thick grass, staring up at a lake-blue world, with wildflowers curled like tendrils around her face. With each passing turn, I glanced at her fingers, her cheeks, her reflection in the side mirror. She fell asleep when we passed the mountain town which everyone thinks is overrated.

Mina woke up when we officially crossed the border, leaving our old world behind. I stopped for fuel at a service station and kept watch for any signs of sudden movement. But despite being in the two-lettered place, I saw no beasts, no creatures—nothing. There were only truck drivers smoking near a picnic table just past the gas pumps. Mina went into the station to use the bathroom. So, I lit a cigarette and found my way over to the men.

"Patience, we've got a live one," someone pointed as I entered their circle.

A man with deep-set eyes looked me up and down.

"Have a seat, boy," he said. "Where are you headed?"

I cautiously sat down on the splintered picnic table. The group was dressed in jeans and sweatshirts. The man called Patience wore a brown vest with a sheepskin lining.

"I'm trying to find the meadow in the sky," I said.

Patience took a long drag on his cigarette and nodded. He spoke as he exhaled a plume of smoke. "You're not far."

"So, it's real?"

He chuckled. "It's on my route. Twice a week I pass the sign."

"Is it safe? It is my first time here and I'm worried about the—"

"They're up there, I won't lie."

"So, we might see one?"

"You might."

The circle of men nodded in agreement. I didn't want to look scared, but Patience could see straight through me. His eyes watered, and the lines in his face told stories.

"The sun stays up late this time of year, but don't let it fool you. When it wants to set, it sinks faster than a stone. Have you got a place to stay the night?"

I shook my head. Patience dug into his pocket and produced a rusted key and a postcard with an image of a large cabin. He told me he was always working and never had the time to use the company lodge. "Someone ought to enjoy it," he said, stubbing out his cigarette. "Take care, kid. You can leave the key under the mat."

When I came back to the car and opened the driver-side door, Mina was eating liquorice and sipping a coffee. A second coffee was in the cup holder along with a candy bar filled with peanuts and sugar. I started to wonder if this was the magic of the two-lettered place.

Just like Patience had said, there was a sign pointing us to the meadow in the sky. I drove slowly through a series of switchback roads until we reached a gravel parking lot. At first, there was no meadow at all. We had to hike through the croaking black trees and needle brush until we found a crooked white-washed cabin and an expansive lake. The water was a reflection of the clouds and cold to the touch. Mina stripped off her clothes and waded past the reeds and tall grasses until she was submerged up to her neck. I scanned the horizon and listened for snarls, but there was no sound except for a woodpecker knocking its beak against a birch tree. I pulled off my shoes, socks and then everything else. I felt mud squish between my toes and sharp blades of grass brush against my forearms. Mina paddled in a circle, calling for me, as her hair trailed down her back like a brush dipped in ink. We stayed in the lake for a long time. We floated on our backs while holding hands. We kissed underneath the water while blowing bubbles from our noses. I pulled her pear-like hips around mine and clutched the pebbles of her ankles. A fish swam between us and Mina caught it with her bare hands. Its slippery silver-green scales shimmered like a rainbow, and Mina brought the glassy-eyed fish to her lips, kissed it once and let it swim away.

Mina slept softly beside me. Through the cabin window, the lake was pulled up like a blanket to the lip of the jagged mountains and I watched purple meadow flowers open their buds to the sunlight of the morning. I quietly slipped out of bed, pulled on a pair of sweats and padded into the small kitchen. The floor was cool, and the cedar beams bathed the room in a honey-yellow glow. I flicked the coffee maker on and pointed the remote at the small television mounted above the kitchen table. A news anchor babbled as I poured coffee into a chipped mug and wondered if Mina really meant what she said last night. I breathed in the long pregnant silence of the sunrise.

"I thought you didn't like mornings," a voice said. I turned to see Mina standing in the kitchen wearing my T-shirt and a lace bottom. She collected a mug and poured herself a coffee, adding three teaspoons of sugar. The scene on the television changed.

A reported sighting has Animal Control searching the streets. People are warned to stay away from the area.

"Turn it up," Mina said, rushing over. She sunk into a chair, and we stared transfixed at the scene on the screen. An image of a hulking animal flashed. It was stumbling up a busy road, weaving through parked cars and growling at lamp-posts. It pushed over a garbage bin, sending trash tumbling into the streets.

"It's the beast," Mina whispered.

"I recognize that shop," I said, pointing at the screen. The beast wasn't in the meadow in the sky. And it wasn't in the two-lettered place. It was passing by Spirit Leaf and the restaurant with the cleaver for a name. "That's my street."

"I can't believe it," Mina exclaimed.

We watched silently as cameras and helicopters followed the beast. Media reporters stood at a distance, but the beast caught their scent and pursued them with angry growls. A cameraman jumped into a shop. Soon, a vehicle approached, and six men in khaki uniforms pointed their guns and shot at the beast.

"They're killing it," cried Mina. But the beast reared and scampered away, moving so quickly that the men with guns lost sight of it. The news reporter flashed on the screen again and spoke earnestly into the microphone.

"What's going to happen?" Mina turned to me.

"I don't know."

On the drive home, we discussed the fate of the animal. I thought about what it was doing on my street. Why was it so far from the two-lettered place? Had it come looking for me?

Mina didn't speak; she nibbled on her nail instead. Outside, it started to rain, and I clicked on the wiper blades. The meadow was in the far distance now, and ahead of us was endless charcoal pavement speckled with vans and long-haul trucks. Black forest trees bordered the highway and passed by us in a whir. The prickly green-blue branches made it difficult to see beyond the edge. How many beasts and creatures live together in that world? Are they afraid of us too?

Sometime in the late evening, we arrived at our city. The street-lamps blurred orange and cast shadows over the wide roads, which everyone believes aren't wide enough. I dropped Mina off at her condo, which is glass, and I kissed her again until I lost the feeling in my toes. As I made my usual left turn home, I found my street was barricaded with orange signs and flashing warnings. A police officer stepped out of his vehicle to halt me and asked me to provide identification proving I belonged. He pressed his hand on my car roof and lowered his face to my open driver-side window. He issued a warning. "There is a wild animal on the loose and it hasn't been caught yet. Be vigilant."

I nodded and pressed the button to reel the window up. I accelerated my car slowly and watched pedestrians dart across the road. Some carried bells. I found a parking spot a block from my building, and I turned off the ignition and paused. I gathered the liquorice wrappers and empty paper coffee cups and wondered if I might dream of fish and pear-shaped hips.

On my short walk home, the shadows stretched and bent between buildings. I darted my eyes to the vacant spaces and gripped my bag tighter. There was a scraping of metal in the distance, but I ignored it. I took the familiar shortcut through the alley to the side door of my apartment. As I inserted my key into to lock, the scent of rotting garbage spilled over my nose, and I thought of the bottle picker who collects large sacks of Pepsi cans and exchanges them for coins. I fumbled to unlock the door and forgot about the jingling of metal-on-metal. I pushed into my apartment, clicked on a lamp and walked past the rock sofa, ignoring the dishes still soaking in the sink. Instead, I stepped out on the balcony and into the warm evening air. I clicked my lighter and leaned over the railing, inhaling smoke and happiness. But from my vantage point, I saw something wasn't right. The bottle picker wasn't in the bin looking for Pepsi cans. It was something else entirely. Something with fangs and fur.

I reached for my phone and hit record.

The lost beast slammed into the side of the bin. I peered over the edge, careful not to scare it. The creature was eating orange peels and nosing through plastic bags. A moment later, it ripped open a bag full of spaghetti noodles and chomped at the rubbery pasta. It tossed a bagel out of the bin, which landed on a blue Hyundai parked a few feet away. Soon, I could hear voices. The metal banging was drawing attention from other balcony dwellers, and I wondered how long I would watch the beast feast on cake and watermelon rinds.

But it was only a few minutes.

A shot echoed.

The hungry creature with noodles on its nose fell silent. I held my phone steady, wondering what would happen next, but nothing happened. A window slide shut. A channel changed. A video ended. But I was transfixed by the hulk of fur in the bin. How could this be the end? I sent the video to Mina, and it only took twenty minutes before she was next to me again. I told her I didn't understand this place, that all I wanted were hips and flowers and fish and pebbles, and somehow, even though we were suspended by concrete above the beast we feared in the two-lettered place— we found the meadow again.

Chelsea Welsh

Portrait of a Lily

The tired pasty background of the canvas
stretched over its thinly structured frame.

Blooming out of it, a large grasping,
flourishing, fully developed lily.

A violet-streaked stretch of petals reached
out grabbing the easel, searching for escape,

crowned by protective yellow-green long leaves
that blurred into the white space, seeping back

into its budding place
frightened to its roots.

Three red pollen lines rest,
raised within the centre.

The only clear indication
of the showpieces creation,

an organic tool.
Your inspired fist.

Ky Mason

if there is a place

pour la langue que je trouve
en Saskatchewan
and in the immersion we learn
through prairie ideologies
et nos histoires
embedded in street names and
    buildings
notre langue continue
d'agrandir, being used
being loved
par des enfants
(des étudiants)
qui ne sais pas des autres langues
pour décrire cette amour

if there is a place
c'est içi, pour notre langue

Ky Mason
s'il y a un endroit

for the language that i find
in Saskatchewan
et l'immersion que nous apprenons
avec les idéologies des prairies
and our histories
écrit dans les noms de nos rues et
    nos bâtiments
our language continues
to grow, utilisé
aimé
by children
(students)
who don't know other languages
to describe this love

s'il y a un endroit
it's here, for our language

Alan Hill

Only Natural

On that Sunday afternoon
when the violence overwhelmed us
my brother's schizophrenia spawned an intensity,
a difference,
too overwhelming for my old-world parents, with
their 'lets keep it normal,' philosophy …

I left the house, sprinted into the fields,
skirted abandoned farmyards, broken tractors, garbage
moved from the edge of our civilization
into wilderness, into forest
up to the mountain's cool lip
into clearing, ferns, ingesting grasses.

I saw the Fox before it saw me
I saw how the scrubs, the trees gave way to it
the air bent, bowed in subservience around its feet.

I smelt the whiff of scat

saw its certainty of risen claw, the
clarity of its bestial self.

How I hated it, wanted to take a rock to its head,
have its pelt.

Katherine Koller
Skunked

Content warning: domestic abuse reference

In this northern Alberta town, Janna and I have a pact: we go to the party together, and together we leave. Everybody's moved here for the same reason—great pay—but the guys here have seen a trillion more trees than women. They work at the same oil and gas job sites, drink and dope up the same, throw around the same greasy money. Black hoodie, black ball cap, full beard, big—that's the guy I last saw talking up Janna at this party-house devoid of furniture, probably abandoned.

I'm done, I text, woozy. I reach for my drink.

Her reply beeps: *I'll get home later with Josh.* Josh has sergeant stripes tattooed on one side of his neck. Probably paramilitary. Janna goes for that. Me, I like a guy who looks you in the eye. Unlike the dude with the red grizzleface sitting on the floor beside me casting sideways glances.

Stay safe, I text back.

You too.

Three a.m., I'm outside waiting for a cab. Frigid fall air, but I'm a blob of molasses. Twelve-hour shifts in Emerg the last four days with the usual stab wounds, overdoses, stitches on the face from bar fights and girls out of it from Rohypnol. Didn't even finish my second cooler but I feel stoned. Wait, was I roofied? I need to hold on to the signpost, steady myself on the newspaper box. I should not have put my drink down, but I need both hands to text, which

I do now, sloppily. *Cab acoming.* Our other roommate rule: if we do get separated, like tonight, we text each step of the way home. No matter what. Should have said, *Drink spiked,* and stayed put, but Janna would have had to pick me up off the floor, and she and sergeant Josh looked promising with all that neck nuzzling. First one who's ever gotten that close since her ex almost strangled her.

I almost hit the ground getting in the cab. I say my address and then I doze off. I know this because when I come to, my head a boulder, the driver pulls me out into the dark.

"Where are we?"

"A party," he says. "You're a party girl."

"I'm a nurse."

He laughs and steers me to a door he pushes open before shoving me inside. I sink to the floor and don't ever want to get up, my limbs glued to the wood planks, my eyes puffed.

"Water," I gasp.

But he's gone. The door slams. I hear a padlock jammed shut. My ears work better than my eyes or my arms that try to sit me up. I take big breaths. I know I have to dilute whatever I ingested. I crawl over rough planks to a fridge, a white beacon in the dimness, but it's roped open, dark inside, disused. From the tap, only a squeak, no water. I smell charred wood before I see the fireplace. I take in the cab's headlights, glaring through the window, projecting a shadow of me on the wood panel wall, until my eyes, slits from the swelling, finally focus.

I use the wall as my guide and creep to the back. I find a bathroom with a toilet that won't flush, make myself puke into a bucket, find a ratty towel to wipe myself off, then try a rear door—locked from the outside—and an empty room. In the deep dark, I wiggle the frame of the window. It's been reinforced by a board on the slider so I pull that away, rip off the screen and listen. Wind in the trees. Leaves rustle off the ground. Temperature dropping. Scent of snow coming. Cab motor still running out front. I don't remember what he looks like. Only a cologne, sharply spicy like the smelling salts we use on the ward for the chicks who come in totally out of it. The sound of him spitting, then whispering, "Party girl."

But I'm not. I'm the one who finds excuses not to go to parties. Janna, she's into dressing up, meeting people; after what she's been through, I'm not going to stand in her way or send her off alone. At the very least, I try to live up to the line I gave her when we moved here last spring: "North, where folks are more honest. Where you can trust people to care about each other." After all, it's frozen six months of the year, so you have to depend on others to help you change a tire in a storm, let them use your phone, say good morning when it's thirty below. "And spill the best spots for cross-country skiing, hiking and camping." Fresh out of training, we both found jobs and bought skis, hiking boots and a tent.

I poke my head out the window. Breathe in deep to clear my mucky brain. Only way to get out is headfirst. Nothing to stand on. I stretch my shoulders and arms through and bend my middle over the metal ledge, but it hurts too much, so I drape my hoodie over it and use it to slide out, brace the window frame with my stupid spiked heels, reach to break the fall, make as little sound as possible. I land on gravel, tug my hoodie back on and head for the woods through a skinny deer trail, up a little hill. I sweat and shiver and hang on to branches as I climb until I find a rock bigger than me. Damn these shoes. "Sexual shoes," Janna said while we were priming with vodka and orange juice. "Go ahead, borrow them tonight. We're cabbing, right?" Even though my mantra is *only wear shoes you can run in*. Never again.

My phone is out of range, but there's a text from two hours ago. That must be how far out of the city I am. *Heading home now. Josh has an early shift.*

Wow. Janna and Josh. I drop behind the rock and see Janna when I picked her up two years ago. Early morning in her kitchen but enough light to detect marks on her neck again. He's not up yet. She's making him coffee. "That guy?" I say. "He doesn't get coffee." I pour it down the sink.

Then I take her hand and her bag and her coat and drive us five hours north.

Maybe she's over it. Maybe early-shift Josh is okay. Maybe.

Another old text from Janna. *Where TF are you?*

To get to the main road, to cell service, to Janna, I need to follow the gravel road past the driveway.

I hear another car coming in. I stop breathing to listen. Shuffling steps, almost dragging. The lock. The cabin door opens, the shove, the fall. The door closes, the lock again. There's another girl in the cabin.

Motors off, the two drivers talk. I smell the stink of their cigarettes. They laugh. Their words don't reach me, but they slap each other's backs like brothers.

Back down the hill path, to the open window at the back of the cabin. I throw a pebble in. She's sobbing, but she hears it. She's not going to fit through the window and doesn't even try. I recognize her from Emerg, but her eyes don't remember me. The slash on her cheek is still healing. Fifteen years old. Beer on her breath. She's wet her pants.

Almost without sound, I say, "I'll get help."

She screams and points.

"What's that?" One of the men calls.

Behind me, a skunk. I take hold of a broom leaning by the back door as the men charge around the corner of the cabin. I sweep and fling, and the skunk lands a short distance at their feet, snarls and salutes. The putrid chemical smell of sulphuric sour crude envelops the woods.

"Aargh!" the men shout. One of them rushes toward me, and I run out of my shoes up the deer path.

The skunk follows me. One man has the broom, as if to whack her, and she pauses to look back, tail raising again. The other man pulls him back; he drops the broom and they streak away from the stench. I try to photograph the cars to get their numbers, but it's too dark, I'm too slow and I get nothing. The skunk looks me in the eye as she passes me, graceful, her tail undulating, wavelike and free after its stiff assault on our senses. I think she's a female skunk. "Girls gotta help each other," I whisper after her. I pull my hoodie over my nose. Eyes stinging. Throat closing up.

The girl inside coughs, swears and calls out to me to hurry, then shuts the cabin window tight.

My legs are rubber but stumble back down the path for my shoes and up the driveway to the village road. Wild snowflakes dive down. I swallow as many as I can.

I keep on, blind until the highway, a black strip down the flat white prairie. The snow hypnotizes me. I feel like lying down and letting it cover me up. Old texts beep in on my phone.

Talk to me!

Where are you?

Are you alive?

What happened?

Communicate.

As soon as I scroll down, some new ones.

We're coming to find you, Josh and me. Your phone says you're west of the city.

We're driving. Hang on.

Please be okay.

I'm here. I step east, toward the sun barely showing behind a thick curtain of snow.

Thank God. We're going slow, it's a whiteout.

I see lights up ahead. A light on top of the car. A cab? I get ready to run into the bush.

Watch for our red light.

It stops blinking when Janna opens the door. She has water and a blanket and bundles me into the backseat with her arms, her body, close. I can't stop shivering.

Janna says to me what we say to all the girls, "You're gonna be okay."

"Yeah." And I hang on to that, what she said. "Josh is a cop?"

He gets the girl and the cigarette butts and the locks, and then we go to Emergency. Janna insists on getting us tested before the drug wears off. I've got abrasions on my arms and legs and face, my feet are a mess, and Janna takes care of me while Josh takes a statement from the girl.

I'm next.

Willow Loveday Little

On Autopsies

Xenia,
It hurts.

The hangman tightens his rope
Against this morning,
Funnels it into your name
Fern-noble in a green that dimples noose.
Xenia. Taste the air—
Its resin, its cure. Each breath is preserved
By miasma as I traipse
A red carpet of my own making.
Religion exists
Only if it is performed and
I strut accolades,
A printshop girl
With Academy Award armpits.

In truth, I'm proudest split open on a table.

The morgue goes beyond—gets authentic.
Its formaldehyde tongue is curious.

A master apparition,
Surgeon with a priest's bedside manner

Carves a Y-incision in my chest,
A spreading yew tree whose
Blackened resin extends into genesis,
Vitals opening to confess their shame
The scalpel's glint a last rite:
Bone saw and winking forceps
Anomalies discovered like
Some Harrison Ford in khaki
Shorts, lassoing himself through dying
Cells, a portal to the organized chaos
Of anatomy.

When you have been slain,
The body remembers.
Blood rings oasis, marks the garrison's bridge,
Pales the lush desert vegetation
In mosquito's breath, extinguishes
The firebirds who brand golden apples,
Gasoline-plumed. Their beaks suddenly forensic.

Rigor-mortis is the body's last defence
Against surrendering its secrets.
Xenia. They're coming. Listen close.
The most dangerous thing about me
Is my need to be a martyr.

A clot of earth. My spilling. This limpid coma.
A bent-browed father gives me away,
A new mother fleshing trauma against my ego
Hammers passiflora into my palms.
Something old, something new. A resurrected adage.
Powder me noose-bruise blue.

I blush safe words,
A bride shedding her skin
On the wedding night,
Trembling kernels of aurora
From oblong mouths of evening red,

As if she didn't know.

Finnian Burnett

Superhero Shoes

Content warning: violence, homophobic slur
You were assaulted in America by a man wearing superhero shoes. The concrete under your head was hard, harder than the kicks he delivered to your ribs and head. You couldn't see his face, but you remember those shoes. Wonder Woman, Aquaman and Superman repeatedly flashing in front of your eyes as you curled into a ball to protect your body from the excruciating blows.

And now the ugly cop, the one with the wart on his nose, wants to know your name. You tell him your true name, but he shakes his head and demands a different answer.

Astin, you say again and again, but he keeps shaking his head.

The other cop, the handsome one who smiles at you with a mouth full of unnaturally white teeth, touches your shoulder. *Your name is Sarah*, he says, and although his tone lifts at the end, as if he's asking a question, he doesn't want a different answer. You stare at him while the other keeps asking your name.

Astin, you say one last time before you finally stop answering. The nurse comes in and forces them to leave, and the next thing you register is lying in your childhood bed back at the little house in Abbotsford.

Your mom serves you chicken soup in a plastic bowl with little gold flowers on it. It's the first time you've seen her since you moved out two years ago. She's lost weight, which emphasizes the recently formed dark circles under her eyes. She hasn't looked this tired since your father died almost ten years ago.

That's my girl, she says. *That's my girl.* She says it until you want to scream, but your head hurts too much to correct her. She calls you Sarah, tentatively at first, then louder. *That's what I named you*, she says, crying. *How could you throw it away?*

You turn to stare at the wall, and the weight of her disappointment crushes your body almost as much as the injuries.

When you're allowed to get up, you pull your old posters out of the tiny closet. Superman. Wonder Woman. Aquaman. The Flash. You plaster them all over the walls. The Justice League. There's no justice, though. The ugly cop calls to tell your mom there are no leads. He wants to know if you remember anything else, and she says no.

But you do remember. You remember your own blood and those superhero shoes and how your head bounced against the sidewalk in the way your mom bounces you from appointment to appointment. Sometimes you can't remember the word for milk, but you can remember those superhero shoes with the drooping laces. You can't understand how someone donning the Justice League could beat up a stranger.

Your therapist asks you to remember what he looked like, what he said. She calls you Astin and reminds you that your mother's disappointment isn't your responsibility. She believes you will be able to move back into your own apartment soon. You want to believe her, but while getting ready for the appointment, you had forgotten how to button your shirt. After fumbling for fifteen minutes, you simply gave up and put on a Superman T-shirt instead.

You walk into the kitchen, and your mother is sitting at the table with a hopeful look on her face. She's going through a box of your old things. *You remember this*, she says. *You were so happy then.* She picks up your old cheerleading outfit. You can't remember the name of your favourite TV show anymore, but you suddenly remember the scratchy material of that tiny skirt and the way the football players would whistle when you walked by in the hall. You remember the weight of the sweater dragging your shoulders to the ground. You remember your best friend's face the day you told her you thought you weren't meant to be a girl.

You can't remember what the perpetrator of your assault looks like, but you can remember the way your best friend cried and called you a dyke.

Your mother brings out albums full of pictures of a little girl whose body language tells a story of someone who didn't belong in the skin she was in. You kneel next to your mother and put your head on her lap. She gently touches the shaved spot around your scar and asks where she went wrong with you.

Your therapist says it isn't your responsibility to educate people, but she gives you a book to give to your mom. *Understanding Your Trans Child*. You give it to her with shaking hands, and she bursts into tears. You go to your room and crawl into the single bed, staring up at the Justice League. Superhero shoes kicking and kicking—you remember the way the rubber soles felt on your face and connected with your nose. You remember the way blood spurted from your nostrils as he yelled that he was making America great again. Great the way it was when gays and Jews and blacks hadn't taken over. Great the way it was when Mexicans weren't stealing his job. Great the way it was before Obama made everyone feel welcome, when you were all superheroes. Great the way it was before women like you started dressing like men, acting like men, living like men.

Your mother goes to your doctor appointments and asks the right questions about symptoms, warning signs and medications. You're grateful for her stalwart presence because sometimes you can't remember whether men's pants are measured by waist or hip size or whether you brushed your teeth that day, so having pills pushed into your hand at the right time is a comfort, even when they're accompanied by your dead name.

Your mother doesn't understand, but she is trying in her own way. She drives you to your therapy appointments, though she doesn't go in. She sits behind the wheel of her 1993 Ford and chews gum, probably thinking about the way you disappointed her.

Your therapist tries to help you remember, but you haven't gotten very far. She asks your name and smiles when you say Astin. She asks about your mother and the photo albums. You ignore the question and talk about the superhero shoes and the way you were destroyed by Wonder Woman and Aquaman. You can't remember how you got back to Canada, and you're afraid to tell your therapist you almost believe that you flew there, as if all the superheroes had turned against you, so you had to save yourself.

Your mother turns her head when you come out of the appointment, putting a wall between you two. You stare at her for a moment, taking in her polyester pants and her brown button-front shirt. At forty, she looks like an old woman. Your fingers ache from wanting to reach for her hand. You want to tell her that you think you know how to save yourself, but you can't remember the word to get someone's attention, and before you can think of it, she's driving and muttering about the terrible traffic.

You crawl into your bed and turn to stare at the superheroes on the wall. You can't remember whether to walk on the green light or red, but you remember those shoes. Your fingers explore the sore spot on your head as you stare at Superman. Your body shifts with the weight of your mother crawling into bed with you. She wraps her arms around you, and you turn, pressing your face against her shoulder. You're crying. She's crying. She rubs your back.

I'm here, Astin, she says. *I'm here.*

© Shannon Taylor-Jones, aftermath

© Brandie J. Wright, Early Frost

© Ania Telfer, *Healing in My Wings*

© Nicole Haywood, Keep Moving

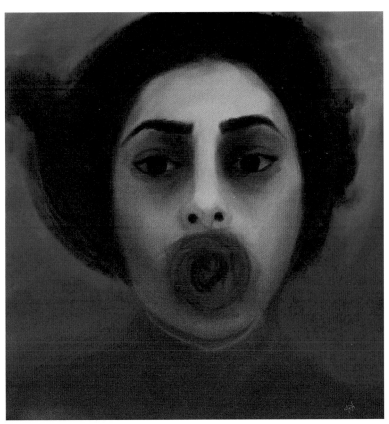

© Taliha Quadri, Rise Ophelia

© Kristin Bjornerud, Memorial

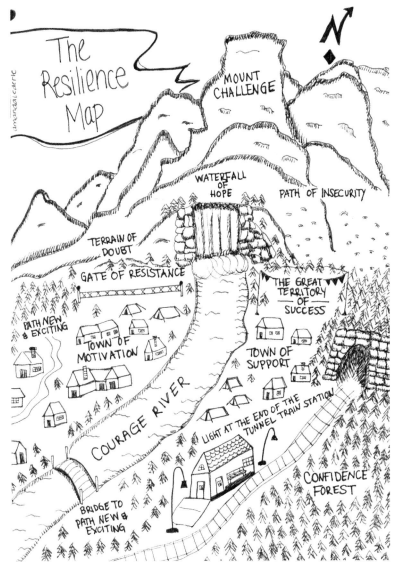

© Amanda Lederle, Resilience Map

K. R. Byggdin

Good Days, Bad Days

Content warning: suicidal thoughts
Today is a bad day.

I awake to find my guts have twisted around me in the night like bedsheets. Knotting themselves into an endless string of worry and fear that refuses to be untangled. To let me rest in peace.

When the alarm goes off, I've been ready to hit the snooze button for hours. Blinking into the dark. Listening to the steady rhythm of your breathing beside me and wishing I could join you. It's the one kindness my body still offers me: turning off my brain when I sleep. No fantasies or nightmares. Just static on the psychic screen. I haven't found the right combo of meds that can do that while I'm awake, not after a month-and-a-half of trying.

The clock on my nightstand is still tuned to CBC Radio One. You asked me to choose a different station after America's last presidential election, when we woke to the incredulous news that the Cheese Puff Bandit had somehow nicked the White House while we slept. We tried contemporary hits, classic rock, even Dal's crunchy-granola campus broadcasts, but none of it seemed right. I had to hear the news.

That's the super fun part about trying to stare down crippling anxiety and chronic depression at the same time—no matter how bad things get out there, I can't stop myself from taking a peek through the curtains. To survey the storm with my own eyes.

We follow the morning routine we've established since I left work. You shower. Pack a lunch for your box-office shift at the theatre on Argyle Street where they keep giving you free tickets to shows we don't attend. Feed the cats. Kiss me goodbye.

I try not to cry. To remember what I have to do today. Just make it through. Go easy on myself. Don't get too stressed. Except, I'm not supposed to use that word anymore. The doctor and HR and the insurance company keep reminding me to call what I'm going through a 'short-term medical absence' and not a stress leave. Not a mental health crisis. Not the bottom of the bottom of the fucking barrel.

I do my best to follow all their rules. Endless cycles of paperwork, appointments, phone calls. To keep them happy. So I can stay off the job just long enough to rebuild enough of me that I can plug back into my old life without blowing another fuse.

The insurance rep with the sugary sweet voice and carefully scripted non-answers keeps calling every few days. Tells me he believes there has been continual improvement, continual improvement, continual improvement. That, with the help of therapy and a handful of prescriptions, I should be back to my old self in no time. What he really means is that it's time to get my file off his desk.

Yesterday was supposed to be a good day. I woke up feeling uncharacteristically light and hopeful. Thought maybe the new meds were finally kicking in. Took a walk outside for the first time in two weeks. To the supermarket on Quinpool, so I could surprise you with dinner. A store that's trying to save the planet by banning plastic bags, forcing unprepared shoppers to wedge their individually shrink-wrapped groceries in pockets and under armpits for the long walk home.

This time, I remembered to bring one of your canvas totes. That you really liked the organic, free-range chickens they sell there. I found one for half-off and paid at the self-checkout with the credit card that gives me store points. There were plenty of cashier lanes open, but I was afraid I'd forgotten how to make small talk. Still, I felt like I had won the Blue Nose Marathon when I got home. Like I had finally found my way back to who I was before all this started. The quiet breakdowns at work. The hyperventilating on street corners. Before the darkness swallowed me whole.

It was only once I went online to balance the card transaction that I realized I'd paid full price for the chicken. I was going to take it back for a refund, but when I checked the bag, I discovered

I had forgotten to take my receipt from the machine. I sat on the cold kitchen floor for the rest of the day, calculating over and over again how much money I'd wasted. Composing apologies to you for going over budget. Getting angry at myself for failing such a simple test. Hating myself for not being able to let it go.

Later, when you found me still clutching the bloody bird and crying uncontrollably, you were very kind. Got me in the shower. Washed my clothes. Ordered us a pizza. Tucked me into bed. I don't plan on telling the insurance rep any of this the next time we speak. It would be like sending him a naked selfie. I have to keep some part of me free from all this prying.

Today, after you leave for work, the cats do their best to rouse me from the bed. Stalking my feet under the covers. Knocking over the little garbage can in the corner and chewing on my snot-filled tissues. Scratching the glass panels on the TV stand in the living room, mewling as the dull thuds of paw-against-door fill the house. Reverberate inside my skull. Get up, get up, get up!

I pick up my phone instead. Play a few mindless games. Check Facebook and Gmail. My therapist has sent a homework reminder. Her messages are always upbeat, full of jargon that is supposed to help. *Practise radical acceptance. Check the facts. Cope ahead.* I wish I had the energy to try, but I'm running on auxiliary power. Everything else had to be shut down. Sensors, communications, defences. All luxuries.

At noon, I cover the clock's accusatory LED display with a dusty copy of a self-help book the library keeps reminding me to return. My stomach growls at me and I scream back at it, silently. I'm at that stage where food would both calm and cause my nausea. I'd rather go hungry than spend another afternoon bear-hugging the toilet.

The cats eventually settle down, burrowing themselves into the crooks of my neck and legs. They do their best to heal me, purring loudly at frequencies which have been shown to combat muscle atrophy and bone density loss in humans. I learn all this when the snooze function on the clock times out yet again and an interview with one of the study's authors comes on. Unfortunately, it seems no research has been done to determine whether house pets have the ability to stabilize chemical imbalances in their owners' brains.

Sometime later I doze off, receiving blissful release for what feels like mere seconds before my phone is buzzing insistently beside my head. It's the insurance rep. I don't answer. Think my vocal cords have permanently fused together. Still, I listen to his message as soon as the voicemail indicator blinks on. Too sick to face him, too scared to ignore him. I wish I had cancer. It would have been so much easier to ask for a longer leave if my wrist had an IV line in it instead of these self-carved scars.

The insurance rep reminds me this is the third time this week I have not answered his calls. He tells me he is worried I am not following my treatment plan. Reminds me I am more likely to experience a successful reintegration to the workplace if my short-term medical absence is not unnecessarily prolonged. That there are plenty of online resources available to me should I require additional support once I return to my job. Finally, he lets me know that my latest extension request has not been approved. I am expected back at work at the end of this week. He does not explain why all the reports I've dutifully collected from my family doctor and psychologist are not enough anymore, or how to appeal his decision. He ends by wishing me continual improvement.

I think about the pills in the medicine cabinet. The ones that are somehow supposed to improve my quality of life by preventing me from drinking alcohol, shitting solids, or getting an erection. I wonder how many of them I would have to take for all this to finally go away. Maybe I'll have to mix them with all the other drugs I'm on. The ones that don't help me sleep. The ones that can't prevent the constant, gnawing pain in my stomach. The ones that try to calm my panic attacks by blanketing my racing heart in the hollow comfort of a numb uncaring fog.

I think about writing you a long letter. Trying to get out in useless empty words how much I love you, you mean to me, you've made me happy. Telling you not to blame yourself but rather a system that still hasn't figured out how to treat a broken brain with the same care and compassion as a broken leg. Encouraging you to use the rest of the money in our dwindling savings account on something nice for yourself. A new car or a vacation somewhere warm. Or maybe a new mattress, one without a fossilized record imprinted on its foam in the shape of me. Of us. When we were still happy. When I wasn't such a burden.

I want so badly to find the will to get all this down on paper for you, or even record it on my phone, but none of my ligaments or tendons respond to my commands anymore. I try to summon what shred of strength remains to finally get out of bed. To at least shower and put on something nice for when they find me. Eat a last meal. Select a comforting album to play as I drift away. Place a sign on the bedroom door telling you not to come in. To call 911. Let the professionals handle this because they've seen it before. They've got the proper training.

I wonder if the cats will be traumatized when they wake up from their afternoon nap and find I've gone cold. If they'll try to purr me back to life.

Hours later, when you finally come home from your shift and find me in bed, you ask how I am. I say I'm fine.

We go through our after-work ritual. I apologize for leaving dishes undone and laundry unwashed yet again. You stroke my forehead and tell me it's okay, you don't mind, I need to take care of myself. You clean out your lunch kit. Check each cat's litterbox, water bowl, food dish. Then, without complaint, you squish into your sopping raincoat one more time. Trudge back down the street in the dwindling light of another bleak and drizzling East Coast evening. To the supermarket on Quinpool.

I turn off the lamp you left on and listen to the rain pound against the windows as I wait for you to return. When you're done in the kitchen, you bring two steaming bowls of chicken noodle soup and the iPad into the bedroom. We watch a few episodes of our favourite sitcom on Netflix, trying not to spill anything on ourselves or the sheets as we laugh and slurp. When we're finished, you do all the dishes and then fall back into bed, exhausted. I don't tell you about the voicemail from the insurance rep. Add it to the list of things I've failed to do today.

When your breathing grows deep and even beside me, I clutch restless hands to my chest and close my eyes. Hope to sleep through the night this time. Hope tomorrow is one of the good days.

Eimear Laffan
/but/

an addendum to your every fist
to justify emergent bone

heavier than its constituency

a vowel at sea between
two stops, a see-saw

concerto scored
on skin, dissonance

behind each vibrating
/b/ar, waves over

-layed with swell; an eye
to the b/u/ckle of you

-r kn/u/ckle, though it was I
scaling the bath

/tub/, an inverted body
tasting taint, the water

-mark rising by decree.

I sea a saw, I saw a sea.

you have a good eye, you'd say
to me. at the sanctuary

I'd spy an eagle veiled
in the canopy

or a heron on the vertical
of a s/i/ngle leg. I was

bracing to cross
the bar, to employ

the /t/t/t/ongue
to execute

the ultimate stop

Allison Thompson

Digging Out of a Pit

Nonfiction

Content warning: domestic abuse, transphobic slurs, suicide references
Day 0:
The voice on the phone stops listening and starts asking questions. "Does your partner criticize you, put you down or call you names?"

"Yeah, but that's just normal couple stuff, right?" I reply.

"Do you feel frightened of your partner when they've been drinking?"

"No, I'm less worried when she is drunk."

"Does she accuse you of having an affair?"

"Yes, frequently."

"Does your partner contradict the positive things others say about you?"

I take a second. "Yes. She claims they're wrong, and she's the only one who knows the real me." I finally see where this is going. Takes me long enough to realize that this is an abusive spouse checklist.

I had never thought I was in an abusive marriage.

The nice lady on the phone continues: "Does she ever hit you?"

"Only when I can't defend myself."

Fuck.

I get lost in my thoughts. I don't even know if she had more questions.

How did I get here? How did I let it get here? How could I let it get here?

I am a stupid piece of shit.

Two hours later, it's finally time to hang up the phone with the Suicide Distress Line employee. I am sure she has others to talk to, and I need to go back home or else things will be worse.

It isn't uncommon for me to leave or get temporarily kicked out. We both pay the mortgage, but she never hesitates to remind me it's got her name on it. She says it's her right to kick me out. If I claim I have a right to be there, she calls the cops and says I hit her.

I often get kicked out after a fight about some minor thing. Maybe I didn't put the dishes away properly, or perhaps our cat threw up. I don't remember what my offence is, this time, but it doesn't matter. Last year, I spent the evening of my birthday wandering the nearby graveyard, looking enviously at the tombstones. I don't remember how that fight started either. I just remember the envy.

I know I have to get out, but I can't do that now. Right now, I have to go back and pretend this is a normal thing that normal people do. Tomorrow, I can look in the garbage to see which of my belongings she has destroyed while I was contemplating suicide, and formulate a plan.

Day 1:

I find a ruined painting in the garbage. A friend made it for me a few years ago. I really loved that painting. At least since we never have friends over, the artist won't notice its absence from the wall.

I've tried to leave before, but it's never stuck. I've asked a friend if I could move into their basement, and I was ratted out. It did not go over well with my wife. I've tried leaving, with nowhere to go, only to find that as soon as I was out the door, my belongings were destroyed and I was being slandered to anyone who would listen. Currently, I'm unable to work due to an injury, so I am both physically and financially unable to go anywhere. If I'm going to survive this, I need a long-term plan.

I set goalposts for two years from now. I will numb myself and perform my role in the marriage. I will dismiss the intermittent affection that glosses over abuse. I'll squirrel away what money I can and build a new support network of people who have nothing to do with my wife. I need to be honest with these people if we are going to support each other. If I am honest with an existing friend, it can easily make it back to my wife. I don't know who I can trust, so I will start again. I need to make my peace with the marriage ending and mourn the few remaining good parts while I am still here, so I don't feel compelled to return. This needs to be a clean break. I can't expend any more emotional energy in the relationship than is needed to be convincing to her and outsiders. I am going to need all the strength I can muster for the endgame.

Day 34:

I am going to physiotherapy for twenty hours each week for a spinal injury.

My wife starts an argument and launches into me about how she 'knows' I am faking the spinal injury. I ask, "Why would I fake this?" Her reply is that without the extra money, she is not able to go out to eat as much or to travel. I am doing this to force her into a more frugal lifestyle.

Shocked at this bizarre line of reasoning, I try to leave the room to gain some space. She runs up to me and punches me in the spine. I don't give her the satisfaction of seeing me collapse or howl in pain. I know that my recovery has just been set back weeks, possibly longer.

I am still on track for my two-year plan though. That is the timeline that matters. My body is inconsequential.

Day 122:

My spinal injury is healed. I've been working between two and three part-time jobs during my entire recovery. I make a serious effort to make new friends and keep them separate from my wife. The jobs don't pay enough to save a significant amount for an escape, but enough to keep my wife off my back. Bills are paid, and I take her out to dinner, regularly.

I get an unsolicited email from a large oil company, asking if I am looking for a job. It's a job I've done before, for different companies. I know I can do it, but I was happy to leave the industry before. I had hoped to never go back. It was long hours and unpredictable schedules and, more crucially, I was coming to realize I was transgender and knew it would not be a safe place for me to transition. But the pay was good.

This will be a means to an end.

If I suffer through this for a year and a half, I'll have enough to start a modest life on my own, no strings attached.

I take the offer and slog through intensive training for a job I loathe.

Day 178:

I am on a long project, and only see the same four people every day for weeks at a time. Two of them regale me about the time they 'beat a tranny half to death.' They assure me it was okay, though, because 'trannies aren't real people.' Then the other two coworkers laugh, and I silently pray that they don't pick up on any of the clues that I am trans.

Day 377:

I'm working in a remote camp. It's a series of joined trailers housing thousands of industry workers. It's such a depressing place that they do suicide checks every night. Having a stranger enter my room twice a night does not encourage a good night's sleep, or general well-being; especially for someone with two decades of suicidal thoughts and an abusive home life.

It's eerie. As if an entire town is on suicide watch. In my months here, I have seen several gurneys and body bags and have been told there's roughly one death a week. One death a week, in a camp of only six-thousand people.

I go to bed at midnight, exhausted after a twenty-one-hour shift. The door opens at 2 a.m. I lift my head from my pillow. "Thanks for checking in. Nope, I'm still alive. Sorry."

I stay awake for three of the four remaining hours until my next shift.

Day 392:

I am finally coming home from the depressing camp. I've been eagerly counting down to this moment for weeks. I miss home.

My wife tells me not to come home. She's gotten used to me not being there and doesn't want me upsetting her rhythm.

Day 424:

We are having another argument where I am accused of infidelity. My act slips up and I say, "I'm not cheating, but we are both miserable, so why won't you let me leave?"

She replies, "If you ever leave, I will fucking destroy you." She then calls my parents to tell them I cheated on her.

Day 521:
I have some money saved up and some new, supportive friendships. I'm nearing the finish line. Only a couple more months of pain, and I can be free.

I have a strange feeling. I don't have a name for it yet, but it's kind of a 'not entirely dead inside' feeling. It's confusing, but I like it.

Day 576:
My wife is acting strangely. I recognize it. I've caught her in affairs before; I see the clues. I'm not as stupid as she tells me that I am. I collect evidence and set up scenarios that make future evidence collection easier.

Most people would be upset if their spouse was cheating, but I'm excited. She can accuse me of whatever she wants, but she has recent, actual infidelity. If I have evidence, and she knows of it, she is unlikely to enter a slander war.

I head back to work for a few weeks, certain I can get what I need upon my return.

Day 602:
I return a couple days before she's expecting me and find used condoms in the garbage. To her and others, I appear happy to be home. In reality, I am really happy to have irrefutable evidence.

I make a few calls.

At bedtime, I snuggle up to my wife and have the best sleep I've had in years.

Day 603:
I move out while she works.

Day 1000:
Still no significant fallout from the marriage ending. No slander, no trouble. I have wonderful relationships with those close to me. I have rediscovered things that I used to love, back when I loved doing things.

I have started hormone therapy and am living an authentic life. It's been like an entirely new existence, and I haven't really struggled with depression since.

People assume starting hormones was the beginning of my new life, but it was truly the day I left my ex.

I struggled in an abusive relationship for twelve years before my call to the suicide hotline. I thought if I loved her enough, maybe she would stop hating me. Obviously, that is not how these things work. Twelve years in, I was so tired of the struggle that I wanted to end my life. The feeling was so certain. I was used to feeling that I wanted to die. The reason I called is that my thoughts switched from wanting to die to being certain I would die by my own hands. There was a certainty, and it was terrifying. I am thankful I was able to resist.

After that call, I gave myself over for two years of intense, focused struggle and a lifetime of adversity as a transgender woman. The fight will never end, but that is okay.

Life is always a struggle, but that doesn't mean I don't get to set the terms.

Holly Schofield

Plain Sight

Content warning: domestic abuse references, slavery reference
I used to be bothered by the hate in their eyes. It would haunt me. Not these days though. When Marnie brings a new recruit in, I can swing right into the routine, no problem.

This one tromps through the dirty snow ahead of Marnie, eyes wary, head high. "I don't understand," she's saying, like they all do. "Why are we coming back here? I just want to fill out the application and leave. I don't smoke. I don't even want to be around smokers."

She glares at me, and I light another, making sure the smoke blows her way. Better to get them pissed off at the start. "Have a seat. I'm Joanne Mendez, senior evaluator." I gesture at one of the aging sun-bleached plastic chairs. I've got the 'grumpy federal bureaucrat' visage down pat.

The smoking corner is at the end of a stark concrete walkway behind the federal building. A dozen metres away, snow-crusted cars hunch in the employee parking lot. It's so bleak and empty, it's perfect for what we do.

Marnie takes the other chair and makes one of her kindly old-lady faces. "It won't take long, dear. Then we can all get out of this cold." Sweet grandmotherly Marnie, long black hair silvered by trauma, driving a hundred kilometres into Saskatoon every day from Little Birch First Nation reserve, no matter what the weather.

The client sits cautiously. Her mouth's a thin slash, her freckled cheeks three shades paler than my own middling shade of brown. A mittened hand cups the cheesecloth sling that cradles her left arm under her open jacket as she waits. She's used to waiting. Like they all are.

Marnie hands me the paper folder, and I set it on the small plastic table next to the tinfoil ashtray. I pick up the first page. "Emma Sanderson, right? Of Parkland Close?" Get them to agree to the easy stuff first, and soon they'll agree to even the most bizarre things. It's a common technique used by car salespeople, insurance peddlers and, of course, domestic abusers. Before I left him, Josh told me I was trash and I agreed; he said I deserved the blows he gave me and I agreed. My wailing soul bowed its head then as meekly as Emma's does now.

I ignore the teardrop running down her cheek. "First time here? Took the bus?"

Quiet yeses from beneath limp strands of hair shielding her face.

Marnie folds her cable-knit sweater across her chest. She's got to be freezing, but she never wants to take the time to put on a coat, even in winter. She plucked this girl from the queue based on my description and herded her straight out here, doing her job as always.

I continue to run through Emma's history aloud. Finished most of a university science degree before quitting at the request of her boyfriend, one Allan Spinner, who'd felt Emma should help him with the accounting at his failing mechanic's shop. I flick my fingernail against his photo: a slick-looking deadbeat with a sweep of dark hair.

It's a thick file. An escalating frequency of hospital visits, all due to 'falling down the stairs' and 'clumsiness in the kitchen'. A useless restraining order.

"What were you expecting Canada Help Centre to do for you today?" I jerk my chin toward the concrete building that towers above us. Inside, a never-ending queue of clients will be slowly shuffling forward to the counter. "Federal programs can't give you much beyond some temporary housing and a few food vouchers, you know."

"I just ..." She twists in the chair, not sure what answer I'm looking for, not sure how to please me.

Marnie's lips tighten, and the loose skin under her chin shivers.

106

She hates this part.

I butt out the ciggie and harden my voice. "Why'd you agree to come around back? Clearly, this shitty smoking area is not official."

Emma bites her lip and tilts her head at Marnie. "Well, she said I should follow her …"

I twist the cigarette butt a few more times. "You always do what people tell you? Even follow them into a deserted parking lot?"

A flash of defiance now, a hint of the alive, intelligent face I'd seen this morning at 6 a.m., floating in my coffee mug. My skills only work when I first get out of bed, but I'm thinking this one could be a real catch. *If* I can reel her in and land her.

I half-stand and lean over the tiny table, right into her personal space. "Why aren't you asking questions? What's wrong with you?"

"Enough!" She's practically spitting. "If you really want to know, I thought you had a secret way to escape. I guess I was wrong. I won't waste your time anymore." The last sentence dredges up her dignity from somewhere, and she rises, straightening her winter jacket, the stylish kind that offers no warmth.

"Sit down. Now." I wait until she complies, then say, "Listen to your words. You said, 'I thought you had a secret way to escape.' Nothing you saw today in the waiting room or at the front counter told you that. Only your new precog abilities could do that, the ones you've developed since you met Spinner."

"My new what?"

Marnie speaks up, right on cue, voice gentle. "Your precognitive abilities, dear. Think about it. When Spinner set fire to your dresser, you'd moved your photo albums out to your car an hour before. On some level you'd already known he was going to flick that lighter."

"Yes, but he'd just been to see his parole officer. He needed to lash out. It was easy to predict."

I chew the inside of my lip. I need a cigarette, a nap, a vacation, but instead I mentally recite the justifications for doing my job: the latest horrendous abuse statistics, the iceberg tip of cruelty that gets recorded in the courts, the endless government studies on domestic abuse oozing from the third-floor file room. Then I swing the file around so her horrific medical photos face her. "No way. You woke up that day knowing. Admit it!"

She pales so much, her freckles look like tiny bruises. "I've been gone too long. I need to leave." She starts to rise.

I exchange a glance with Marnie.

She leans forward. "Joanne is just trying to help you, Emma. She—"

"Bullshit!"

Now what? This one is stronger and fiercer than I'd realized. I can't let her leave after making her this angry. Not with her skills. She'll head for Spinner and retaliate, like the client last year who went straight home and ran over her abuser with her Ford Fusion, not just once but thirty times. Women everywhere are ready to crack.

To hell with following the script. I toss the file aside. Maybe she'll respond better to science than emotion. "Ever heard of epigenetics and intergenerational effects? How environmentally altered DNA gets passed down to descendants?"

She's listening again, intrigued in spite of herself. "I saw an article. Songbirds near highways change their song over generations to a lower pitch so they can be heard over traffic. That what you mean?"

"Exactly. Or, a human example is Holocaust victims. Their grandchildren have more trouble handling stress than most people due to low cortisol levels and some other things. And, guess what, people nowadays who suffer domestic abuse also develop a genetic setup that—"

"Domestic abuse isn't new. It's always existed." A tight, triumphant smile. "And what about all the other forms of abuse? Torture? Slavery? Other kinds of suffering?"

"Sure, but those aren't my concern. That's a different branch of Canada Help. Here, in this department, the only thing we deal with—"

"Seriously? You're telling me: 'Not my department'? You're so full of shit—"

"Listen! The *rate* of genetic change in spousal abuse victims in Canada is speeding up. We're changing super-fast!"

"And why would that be?"

I shrug. "Who knows? A tipping point in population dynamics? The #MeToo movement affecting our collective consciousness? Frankly, I don't care why. Understanding it isn't—"

"I've had all kinds of counselling, you know. I realize my problems stem from a lack of self-esteem, and with the need to find validation through a relationship—"

"I'm not talking about your problems; I'm talking about your opportunities."

"Yeah, right. If a trauma doesn't kill you—"

"It makes you who you are? No, damn it. Our responses to traumas make us who we are. We still don't wish crap like that on our daughters, do we?"

"Suppose this is all true. So what." Her voice is flat.

I hold her eyes with mine. "Turns out there's a way to train people to enhance those skills even further, increasing a person's range and accuracy. Our little underground group of front-line staff in all the Canada Help offices have developed a team of recruits who have so far prevented two bank robberies and an incel mass attack. We've even recruited a couple of female politicians. It's not unreasonable to assume that we can prevent wars breaking out *if* we have enough recruits. We need you, for fuck's sake!"

"Wait, are you trying to force me into some cult?" Fear pulls at her mouth. She nearly tips over her flimsy plastic chair trying to wrench her purse strap free.

All the pretence drains out of me. I can't do it. I can't keep up the mean bitch act any longer. "Sorry, honey." I lurch to my feet and move around the table toward her. "We both could use a hug …"

She draws back her good arm. "Keep away from me! I'll hit you, I will!"

I step back. "Everything's going to be okay. Honest."

She hears something in my voice. "You were faking your anger the whole time; you were manipulating me! To make me do what you want!"

"No, to make you listen. We need—"

"You're as bad as all of them! You're just another type of abuser!"

"Yes, dear, she is." Marnie's smile is gentle. "Unfortunately, coercive techniques are the only way we've found to get through. People with your strain of precog skill avoid ugly truths until their emotions are ramped-up enough. So, we hire people like Joanne to make that happen." She can't keep the contempt for me out of her voice.

Emma crimps her mouth at me. "You're a real asshole, you know."

"I am." I look into her eyes. "But, hell, our five-year plan is entering its fourth year. We're about to start Phase Two: teaching the non-abused how to bring forth their innate abilities. Knowing an outcome, truly knowing it, is the first step in giving everyone the long-term viewpoint that humanity is so desperately lacking."

Warily, I watch Emma mull things over. Finally, her eyes spark as she realizes what precog skills could mean to the world. I take that glimmer and hold it in my mind. I'll need it tonight alone in my dark apartment.

"Well, shit." Emma turns to Marnie. "Take me to this recruitment camp? Help me find a way forward?" With her good hand, she twists her messy bun up into a firm knot. "I … think I'm ready as long as *you* stay with me."

"I'll help you settle in, dear. There're lots of lovely people involved. Don't judge the department by people like *her*." Marnie places her wrinkled hand on Emma's arm, and they begin to teeter down the snowy walkway together.

At the corner, they can't help but look back. Emma shakes her head and Marnie's lip curls in revulsion.

No, I don't mind that they hate me. It's part of the job.

But I don't know how much longer I can take the look of disgust I see every night in the mirror.

Alejandra Jimenez de Luis

A Prayer to Our Lady of Sorrows

Mother, may the day I unravel start like any other,
An inevitable apocalypse under the burning sun,
Streets heavy with children laughing,
Couples strolling,
Tourists taking pictures of buildings
That will go up in smoke moments later.

Let your hand pull at the thorns around my stomach and slice me
open,
I have spent too long being afraid of my own shattering,
Too wary of who might be in range when the frayed ends of my
body give way.

I have worshipped you, mother
Ran fear through my fingers like an endless string of prayer beads
Counted empty minutes that
Melt into nights sitting heavy on my chest
I seek your mercy in the transcendence
Of my own destruction.

I have held it back long enough swallowed
Lopressor like a communion wafer at a service
I was never baptized into. You
Don't seem to pick your congregation we just

Suddenly find our place in the pews between
Sobs in a McDonald's bathroom or an airport or a
Doctor's office or just
Whenever the first time is.

Make me a martyr, let this feel less
Pointless than it usually does let it be a warning a
Distant toll ringing in the ears of all those of us who
Wear swords around our necks like we're preparing
For a bloodbath that never comes.

Tear away the corpse draped
Over my knees so that my
Mourning might have a larger
Wingspan
so that my Armageddon unrolls
its black streamers into the sky
and trips those comfortably watching.

Let it start quietly, barely noticeably
Let it creep into my quickening heartbeat
Squeeze like a numb hand around my throat
Split my lungs with broken bones

Blur my vision into a shaking
That flattens the landscape.

Mother, may the day I unravel start like any other,
I have rehearsed my death too many times to be unprepared.

Alex Benarzi
The Lies We Tell

It happened at a fast-food shawarma joint. While staring at the back-lit menu above the counter, Abraham Dempsie, a sixteen-year-old with the name of a seventy-year-old, realized he was growing blind.

Growing blind. He would come to hate the expression, as though the dirt pooling at the bottom of his eyes were seeds, the ocular weeds of retinitis pigmentosa.

The woman behind the counter drummed her fingers. "What can I get you?" she asked.

Was she smiling? He couldn't tell. He ordered his lunch through clenched teeth. Being shut off from fast-food menus hurt, but being unable to discern a smile punched him in the stomach, leaving him with barely enough air to thank the woman. He grabbed the wrap and ran to the solitude of his car.

He slumped back, his hands gripping the wheel, the scent of garlic rising from the passenger seat. He twisted the key with a slow turn of the wrist. He was afraid the engine would leap like a startled cat, dragging the car, Abraham and his cooling lunch into oncoming traffic. He felt it—an exhale escaping his lips, failing to be replaced with an intake until his chest tightened and head hurt and sunspots assaulted his itching right eye. He couldn't drive in this condition. He couldn't drive. He couldn't breathe. Was there anything he *could* do?

Abraham closed his eyes and grabbed his lunch. He choked

as the wrap slid into his mouth. But he couldn't swallow the questions: how would he get his father's car home? He shouldn't have taken it in the first place. He opened his eyes to the sign above the restaurant taunting him as its lettering swayed. How could he tell his parents what was happening when he had no idea how to tell himself? Going blind. Growing blind. Stunting his growth. His future. Everything he wanted to do, stolen from him.

He fought through the eye ache, the nascent tears, the heavy breaths. He put the car in reverse, and the car careened toward the pole. Hands clutching the wheel, his thoughts oscillated between anger and strategy. His parents would buy that he was a clumsy driver. Better to think he was clumsy than useless. They didn't need to know that he was finished, that his future as Abraham Dempsie, M.D., had been destroyed by the cellular equivalent of a reckless night out.

The echo of bumper-hitting-metal swirled around him.

Susan searched for the perfect clementine, finding each unsatisfactory.

"This is not something you can keep to yourself," her mother wheezed.

Susan dropped a bruised clementine back into the crate. "I'll tell them when I know more." She grabbed another, pressing her index finger lightly into its skin. It had too much give, but if she ate it right away, it would be fine. She wasn't going to scare her family over nothing.

It was the week before Christmas, and Corrine was already a mess. And how could Susan even think of telling Sage? *Mommy's fine, she just might not be alive in a year, that's all.* Susan abandoned the clementines and tried her luck with the navels. They weren't much better.

"You need lots of vitamin C," her mother chirped, "that's what the doctor said, right?"

Was it? Dr. Lewis spat out so many things so quickly, every word melted against her ears. It didn't matter how many 'caveats' or 'inconclusive tests' he threw at her. It was a possibility. After all she had worked toward, their lives... her life... hung by the nail of possibility like a crooked portrait.

"I just think," her mother's voice impervious to the public setting, "that if you give them the time to prepare, even if nothing happens, it is better than—"

Susan wanted to whip the orange at her mother's face, but instead let it fall into the plastic bag. She should have invested in a reusable fruit bag, better for the environment.

That was her first 'I should've' moment.

Abraham hurled Angela Duckworth's *Grit* across his bedroom. Passion. Perseverance. Overcoming challenges. The promises of a highly acclaimed self-help book meant nothing. His eyes and mind were unable to focus, the blurred words lacking any meaning. He passed his mom preparing dinner and his dad watching TV, out of the apartment for fresh air. They didn't care: their cooling period following the car crash stretched through the quiet Christmas season into the dying embers of the year. Dad's theatrics ("The repairs are coming out of your university funds! You'll never drive again, dammit!") would have made him laugh if the threats weren't coated with truth. He wouldn't drive again. As for university ... he had been so focused on becoming a renowned oncologist or cardiologist—paths now blocked off to him, rendering university meaningless.

He stepped into the empty elevator, shut his eyes and ran his fingers down the faded bumps beside the numbers. Would he need to learn braille? Did blind people still use braille, or was everything text-to-speech? Questions without answers, and no one to ask. He retreated to the back as the elevator jerked to life. The door reflected a distorted face and Abraham saw, in his downturned lips, himself a few years younger, driving with Mom.

They passed a man tapping his white cane along the sidewalk.

"Poor soul," Mom mumbled. "People like that, Abraham, don't have a chance."

Abraham looked over his shoulder. When he would become a doctor, he could help people like that.

People like him.

He couldn't help people when he didn't have a chance. If he didn't have a future. He needed them to believe he had a future. Abraham Dempsie, first-generation Canadian, was supposed to be successful.

Instead, eyes shut, he would spit his parents' generosity into their faces, inevitably missing the mark.

The elevator stopped at the fifth floor, and a middle-aged woman entered. Short, with a massive mound of red curls cascading down her back. She pressed the already lit button for the ground floor, and when the doors didn't close fast enough, she pressed it again and again. Abraham was rapidly losing the ability to see much, but he saw her frustration. His first impulse was to offer some lighthearted comfort. If only she knew that her mundane problems meant nothing. This woman, at least, could drive, read, function independently. His thoughts soured, so he kept his mouth shut.

Susan stood at the counter, chopping onions, the crash of knife-against-board in tandem with her daughter's sniffles. Sage hated the smell of onions.

"They're good for you." Susan knew Sage wasn't listening. Sitting at the kitchen table with her earbuds in, the tablet propped up against a Tupperware container as she watched whatever she did on YouTube. Would Sage remember this day? Ignoring her mother only for ...

Susan couldn't let herself think like that. Sage was happy in her blissful ignorance.

A shiver ran through her when Corrine opened the door to their apartment.

"Traffic." Corrine threw her briefcase and coat on the sofa. "There were two separate accidents. It's like—what?—people forget that snow is a thing every year?" She scurried over to the counter, leaned down and kissed Susan on the back of the neck.

Had Susan experienced her last first snow?

"How was school today, Sage?" Corrine asked.

Sage did not respond.

"Why do we keep her around?"

Susan couldn't keep the chuckle from escaping. For all her flaws, Corrine had that power—laughter, her light in darkness.

"How's your mother doing?"

Susan put down the knife and dabbed her watering eyes with a napkin. Two weeks since she came up with her happy alternative. Her mother was right, she couldn't keep her family in the dark; she didn't have the poker face for it. She couldn't tell them either. But if her mother had just been terminally diagnosed with a severe brain aneurysm ... Corrine drank in the lie: a cocktail of dread and guilt.

"There's a package for you downstairs." Corrine changed the topic, realizing Susan didn't want to talk about it. "The new guy wouldn't let me pick it up. Didn't believe I was family." Corrine

THE LIES WE TELL

hummed Gwen Stefani's *Rich Girl.* "If I had a penis: na-na-na ..."

Again, despite her intentions, Susan laughed.

Package retrieved, Susan stepped into the elevator.

"Hold the door." A teenage boy wearing sunglasses rushed by, using a branch still brimming with leaves as a cane. He shuffled over to the panel and ran his hand over the buttons.

"Can I help?" Susan asked.

"All good." He danced his fingers around the top floors. The doors closed, and the elevator stood still.

"Alright." Susan paused. "Can you hit five?"

"Sure." He jerked his hand down and pressed seven.

"Close," Susan said. "It would help if you took off your sunglasses."

"That's not something you should say to a blind guy."

"I saw you yesterday. You weren't blind then. I think." She recognized him but didn't pay much attention. Surely, she would have noticed his unique choice for a cane.

"I'm practicing."

The elevator scurried past her floor. "Practicing?"

"For when I actually go blind. Any day now."

"I'm sorry." The doors opened to the seventh floor. Susan stood in the doorway, the elevator beeping at her when it grew too impatient. She looked at the boy: probably still in high school. When she was in high school, she was worried about her body and her grades, she couldn't imagine having to deal with such a major adjustment at that age. Even at her age, a major adjustment.

She stepped out. "I'm dying," she said, unsure if her voice made it through the crack of closing elevator doors.

Abraham closed the door to apartment 504, unfolded his white cane and tapped along the hallway until he struck the infinitesimal rise of the tiles signalling the elevators. He was grateful that Corrine had offered to take a stranger to join them in spreading Susan's ashes along the riverbed, even if he was consumed by guilt the entire time. Susan loved Fish Creek Park. Abraham loved it too: long summer walks with his parents. He had dreaded returning, being in that familiar space and unable to see the birds or the boats lazily rolling down the river, rocked by miniature waves. Corrine and Sage had dug the shallow hole that would house Susan's ashes as he'd stood to the side, looking up at shadows of trees swaying across his lenses. In place of a eulogy, Corrine had let loose the volley of vitriol she'd been keeping in.

"Fuck you," she had concluded. "We couldn't even say good-bye." She'd fallen to her knees beside Sage, who offered her mother no comfort.

Abraham had breathed in. It was cathartic. Though she was a shaking shadow on the ground, he saw Corrine clearly.

Abraham had been too wrapped up in himself, using Susan as a therapist and trainer, never questioning why she'd been so eager to help him adjust. He'd grown more confident as she grew weaker. He hadn't seen it until the end, when the illness that Susan had been evading had tapped her on the shoulder and then pinned her to the ground, leaving the newly blind Abraham to get her to the hospital.

Susan had not told her wife or kid that she was dying until it was too late. And in her final moments, when good Catholics repent, she'd smiled and spoken of the wonderful lives they'd had for as long as they'd had them. Abraham, standing in the corner of her hospital room, could only think that he had made the right decision. He had staved off the alienation that invaded his apartment when his parents discovered he couldn't be a doctor. They would have to take care of him for a little longer.

Like Susan, Abraham had a few last great months with his parents. Because of Susan, he had a few great months with them as he learned to contain his hatred for their genes. Unlike Susan, he had time to mend his relationship.

Suzanne Whitney Ghadimi

Topograph

Content warning: domestic abuse, sexual assault references
Sarah was oblivious—or so she was often told—to most things
happening around her. Life just seemed easier that way.
"You are a waste of space," Donald told her one night. She didn't
answer. He may have assumed he could say this because she hadn't
wanted to have sex, or because they had just had sex and he felt
he didn't need to be nice to her for a while. Oblivious as she may
have been, she knew a husband shouldn't think that of his wife.

Working nights was like living with permanent jet lag. That
also might have contributed to her general obliviousness, but it
paid the bills and allowed her husband to enjoy life as a grad
student. She couldn't sleep during the day and often lay awake.

It was spring—the days were getting longer and she slept even
less. She noticed the initial cracks in the ceiling as she lay in bed,
exhausted and miserable. They appeared first in the bedroom.
Their claustrophobic basement suite in Kits only had three small
rooms, but the location was what mattered. Kitsilano was
the place to live in Vancouver in the 90s. The city was becoming
the nirvana of Canada for wealthy foreign investors eager to buy
real estate in a stable country. Everyone wanted to live in the
mild climate of the west coast with views of English Bay. The old
hippies who gave Kits its chilled vibe were slowly being replaced
by venture capitalists, but no one seemed to mind.

The low ceilings of the suite made it easier for her to notice the fine, thin lines that appeared that first day. She got out of bed and touched the cracks that radiated from the corner of the room. They weren't deep; they rested just on the surface of the badly painted plaster and were very easy not to notice. The lines branched and twisted in several directions and only covered a small area. The family upstairs had two little boys—maybe they had been pouring water on the floor? Perhaps their mom had dropped a bottle of wine?

A few minutes passed before Sarah mindlessly got dressed and started the laundry.

"I want to know what you're going to do to make this happen," Donald demanded.

Sarah had a couple of hours before she had to leave for work and was currently stuck in a chair being interrogated. Donald was on about his latest plan to become important, but she really wasn't paying much attention; there would be a new, better plan in a few weeks. She could simply wait it out. She closed her eyes as he ranted and then opened them, glancing at the low, oppressive ceiling in the tiny living room. There were cracks here as well. She stared at them and wondered if he noticed but decided it was better not to ask. She eventually escaped and got ready to leave for her shift starting at 11 p.m.

"Bye, Donny," she said as she left for work, but he didn't answer.

The hospital ER where she worked was the sexual assault centre of the Lower Mainland, and she would sometimes take calls from women who had been raped and were asking what to do. No one had told her what to say or trained her to answer these questions. She was just a clerk.

"Come to the hospital," she would say. "We'll help you, just come." It was the best she could think of. The nurses and doctors had special training. "Oh," she'd sometimes remember to add, "the doctor who will examine you will be a woman, don't worry."

The next morning, she watched as the lines slowly advanced and danced across the ceiling. One line circled the lone light fixture with its sad, bare bulb. Then the line twisted and moved toward the doorway to the small living room. What would happen if the cracks in the living room joined with the ones in the bedroom?

Why were there no cracks in the tiny kitchen by the basement entrance? They grew and morphed into patterns and grids and Sarah wondered, yet again, what it all meant and if she should tell someone that they had appeared.

She walked home slowly from the grocery store one evening. Donald was in a foul mood, and she was in no rush to return.

She came around the corner of the house into the backyard. She had heard the tipsy laugh of Dora, her landlady, half a block away and found her sitting at the rickety picnic table, several bottles of wine and glasses spread about. Sarah's landlord was there too. He quietly smoked joint after joint to make himself interesting and interested. Vancouver in the 90s.

"I can't believe how much money they wasted!" Dora was saying. "He died anyway."

Sarah was in no hurry to enter the basement, and the evening was warm. She still had a few hours before work, so, when invited to sit down at the paint-peeling table, she did. The grocery bags were heavy.

"They paid two full-time educational assistants for years so he could go to school, so he could be part of a 'normal' class," Dora continued. "He probably didn't know what the fuck was going on; he couldn't talk or anything." She worked part-time as a secretary in a local high school and had found out a student at the school had died. She drained her glass and said, "What a waste of money."

Allan, Sarah's landlord, looked over at her and said, "Do you know how much this place has appreciated in the last year?" He said he was thinking of buying a new car. Sarah shifted her gaze to the house and noticed it needed painting.

There was a crash and yelling from inside the house where the boys were. The sound of the TV and stereo both boomed about the backyard. Another crash and a wail of "Mom!" came from somewhere.

"Boys," sighed Allen.

"Thank God we had boys," said Dora. "I would've had to worry about girls getting fat." She poured another glass. "Wine has empty calories," she said as she waved the bottle around.

Lying on the floor, Sarah tried to see all the lines from as far away as possible. Up close, they still made little sense. She had not bothered mentioning the cracks to her landlords the night before; her husband had heard her and came out to join in whatever conversation was happening. He would not be left out. But she couldn't tell them, she couldn't tell anyone about what was going on because she didn't know herself.

She dug around in an old box of hidden, treasured bits and pieces she kept in the back of a dark, damp cupboard until she found an old sketchbook. Lying on her back with the pad and a pen in hand, she began drawing the lines on a piece of paper. Her head was aching from exhaustion, but she drew for a while anyway.

The lines had joined the two rooms together by now, but still nothing appeared in the kitchen. A vein had broken away from the rest and was snaking toward the doorway between the kitchen and living room. She lay beneath that doorway and drew the final bit over what had now become several pages. Sitting up, she looked at the pieces of paper and began moving them around on the floor. She didn't have much time until he would be home, and she needed to start dinner. After shuffling the papers around for a bit, she folded up the pages and put them in her purse for safekeeping.

One night, she took a call from a woman at 3 a.m. The ER was throbbing with patients and staff. It was barely managed chaos.

"Hello, ER," she said.

There was a long pause. "Hello … I think I need help," a woman said.

"Okay, what can I help you with?" Sarah asked, gently.

"I was raped."

"Come to the hospital, there are trained doctors and nurses to help."

"I'm scared."

"It's okay, just—"

"No, I'm scared no one will believe me," the woman said as her voice broke.

Sarah didn't know how to answer. This wasn't something that had been said to her before. A nurse was yelling at her for the blood work of the patient in bed three and the other line was flashing, but she thought for a few precious seconds.

"I believe you," she said, but the line went dead.

Eventually the day came when the crack appeared in the kitchen and crossed in an almost straight line to the basement door. She felt scared when she saw it. It was a deep crack, deeper than all the others. A meaningful crack. She was sitting on the kitchen floor adding this last bit to her drawings when he came in. She hadn't expected him for a while. He was angry and demanded her complete attention, so she settled in a chair, feeling trapped as she listened to his monologue of discontent and disturbed accusations against her and the world. He deserved so much more, he kept saying.

She was surprised when the book hit her face.

"Fucking look at me!" he yelled at her.

Sarah sat, stunned. She could usually see the violence coming. Then, as quickly as the book had hit her, she stood. She was halfway out the door with her purse, her keys and her precious papers when he caught her. He slammed the door into her back, the doorknob hitting her hard.

"Fuck you," he said as he grabbed the keys from her hand, opened the door and shoved her through. "You won't get far without—" he started to say, but she didn't stop to listen to the rest.

She stumbled up the three steps to the backyard, her back aching. Pain and awareness branched out and into her. He slammed the door, and she heard the lock click. She'd have to beg him to let her back in. She leaned against the wall for a moment and unwillingly overheard Dora on the phone: "Can you believe she wore that? How could she? Jesus, you'd think she'd never looked in a mirror." She didn't need to see the wine glass in Dora's hand to know it was there. The boys were yelling, ignored, in the background. They had lived on top of each other for too long.

She looked at her drawings, her documented cracks. She looked at the line to the door then turned the piece of paper around. That line, the last line, didn't lead to the door; it was the path away from it. It was the map to the rest of the world, and it led far from this place.

He's wrong, she thought, *I'll go far.* And she began to move away from the darkness of that basement, that house of greed and malice. She held in her hands all she needed to escape from Vancouver in the 90s.

Everything else, she would leave behind.

Christa Marie Burgin

Bottled Up

Nonfiction

Content warning: depression

You count the bottles by your bed—deceptively empty, filled with tears instead. Drink 'em up. Choke 'em down.

It's the start of another day.

Another day with a brave face—that façade to distract from the crumbling foundation—but that only comes after the biting, bitter taste of the sorrow you've swallowed up. That's all you are, after all, a walking cliché—a side effect of life after loss. Your loss, and now you're lost. Lost in thought and the pain you've brought about yourself.

You've earned it, of course; you took out a loan on happiness—spent it in your younger years on misdoings and misdeeds—and now misery is helping you repay your debt.

And you can't help but wonder: Is this what it means to grow up and apart? Are you doomed to rotate through memories of misery? Is the real world just a cage in your head and the incessant fear that those who love you are all just pretend?

You wonder and you want to turn off your thoughts, but instead they only turn, a waterwheel rotating inside your head, buckets of insecurity pouring over you again and again and again and ...

You just don't know when it will end.

The hatred ...

Selfish.
　　　Stupid.
Such
　　a
　　　　waste.
　　　　　　　Loathing ...
　　　　　　　　　　　Failure.
　　　　　　Fuck-up.
　　　　　　　　Complete disgrace.

　　　　　　　　　　　Emptiness ...
　　　　　　　　　　　　　Pathetic.
　　　　　　　　Garbage.
　　　　　　　　　　　　Insignificant.
The levels in your bottles continue to rise, and a new word then comes to your mind: *dismal*. Strange how it reminds you of who you used to be—a shy little girl in pigtails and jeans, swimming through life without a thought in her head—and who it was you might have been had you just found a way to be *okay*. A parallel you ... but she doesn't exist.

Because the girl you were was always you, just at a time before you knew that the word in question would consume your mind. A fascination that'd devolve to obsession, to a realization that the term drew you in because you understood what it meant. A word without definition, only feeling.

And so, you had kept it tucked inside until one day there came a time to share the surge it gave you. Your intro to an Intro Writing course was the request to share your word of choice. Your hand had reached the air before those of your peers, and you'd approached the canvas as the first volunteer. Whiteboard, blue marker, favourite word: *dismal*.

Your professor had seemed a bit perplexed, and you immediately fumbled when you tried to express that what drew you in was the way it sounds, the way it sounds like what it means, the way you say the word and feel it and ...

He said he understood what you had meant, but the stares from your classmates instead went right through you. They shifted uncomfortably within their seats, each of their looks producing a heat that burned through your chest, the word screaming like a siren inside of your head—*Dismal! Dismal! Dismal!*—until you shook with its rhythm.

Was it the rhythm or the worry that stole your words then? That made you feel small and made your voice smaller? You shivered in your seat as a smog filled your mind, covering your words until you felt blind.

At times you think you've found the expressions to explain the pressure building in your head, the spiderweb cracks spreading across your chest. Scribbled down, folded up; pages of phrases forgotten in the highs, rediscovered in the lows. They pull you lower, the words you inevitably hate. You lay them out, strings of phrases stitching together the battered patchwork of papers. A fabrication of lies meant to make you feel okay. They never do, but still you wrap yourself up in that paper-cut quilt.

You know, of course, that you have to let go. So, you slither from the mattress to the floor—a bit like a snake shedding its skin from the day before, though that would imply that you feel reborn.

And you don't.

What you feel instead is a collection of re's: resigned, regressed, removed, repressed. But above all else, reflex. You've set your life into a loop, a rhythmic routine of heartbroken habits (pity, shame, dolour, distress); it's simply now a game of roulette. Bad chances, no luck, but this isn't your first gamble—the bottles alone are evidence of that.

Sharing your favourite word with strangers had clearly been a risk, but you thought perhaps you could expect more from a friend. And so, you'd decided to try again with a *Whiskey Lullaby*, but your explanation came out a sticky mess: The words might be sad, but they mean something, they mean something because they make you *feel* something. Something ...

That's just depressing.

Your not-friend didn't even miss a beat and made sure you knew how much of a drag you were. A downer, a dud. What you realize now—what you never knew then—was that sadness had approached you in the guise of a friend. You listened to her sombre songs and soon began to sway along until the darkness seeped into every inch of you. Not that you ever had a clue. You craved her affection, vied for her love. Gathered your bottles, poured yourself out, and for what? A relationship with no return.

Her fury grew in the silence. When you weren't quite enough, whenever you slipped up. Did you know you were that bad a friend? (*Didn't* you know you were that bad a friend?) Well, now you do; she'd made sure you knew that you deserved every ounce of sadness.

You don't remember exactly when—when you'd started suffocating between your breaths, and your memories had morphed into flashes of regret. You don't remember exactly when, but it seemed to have escalated with the loss of a friend.

Could you ever rewind? Do it over again? You interrupt the routine, as you do now and then, and pull out the box of broken bottle bits, the slivers and shards of ruined relationships. You dig down deep, rummaging around for the pieces that match, wincing and wondering through the pain: Why'd I have to go and break 'em all up?

But your search to salvage what you smashed apart leaves you empty-handed. Bloody fingers. Broken heart. The damage you caused simply can't be undone. At least, that's what she'd told you, your not-friend. Your pain is your right for being so wrong. Good intentions wrapped in misdeed, you're doomed to repeat the process again.

Why, your mother now asks inside your head, *do you think so little of yourself? Why do you always put yourself down? Why can't you just be happy with who you are? Why? Why? Why?*

She'd said the words intending kindness, but they'd sounded like a threat. And while you knew that wasn't really what she had meant, they still seemed to have come out all bent—up, out of shape ... hell. You felt yourself shrinking, becoming less than, undone and none. She berated you with kind words until they mimicked the violent tune playing in your head. Questions and questions, again and again. No answer. No words. You couldn't stop them from swirling through your mind, so you packed up some things and then you fled, spent a week in hiding with a friend.

You eventually returned home to silence and were reminded again of the wrath that grows in its empty space. And while the years have moved on, your mother has not. *You hurt me.* I know. *You hurt me so much.* She says it in a way that seems like there's more, but perhaps you will never really know because you can't seem to throw together a sentence, can't find the words bottled up.

I'm sorry.

That's all you can say. All you can ever say. She gives you a look, and you remember how people seem to like you less when they smell the apologies on your breath. Yet the words trickle out, a leaky faucet of stunted vocabulary from years of trying and failing to be better. To be more.

And sometimes you think you could be—would be—if only you knew what to do with those broken bottles and the cracks in all the others. Of course, that feeling comes in waves, comes in slowly on the days when you feel okay. When you remind yourself that you don't deserve to feel this way. You're happy now, remember? You are, it's true, but what's disturbing is that you somehow still feel a pit. An abyss disjointed from your current happiness. An incessant fear that any bottles miraculously still intact will soon be covered into dozens of cracks. That one day you'll tap them, and they will all fall apart.

You won't, of course. You will shatter instead. As it is, you constantly manage to find chips and splits—inevitable, given how you treat yourself. There's at least one piece you've held on to for years, a part of yourself that's fallen out of place, its shape worn down like a worry stone.

You'd like to—*need to*—worry less, let go of the pain and the fear and the stress. Pull out the pieces of pain ripping through your chest and the slivers of throbbing memories that have infected your head. You've tried so long to wait it out, starve it until it leaves, but it always manages to find you in your sleep, wrapping you up in the mournings.

But you're starving now too, wasting into nothing as you crave for something more. There must be more, a part of you buried beneath your swallowed-back tears. You can feel her—you—closed up inside, trying desperately to speak between her suffocated breaths. Can you hear her?

You still have no voice—a little mermaid lost in her pigtailed head—so all you can do is write instead. You listen for her voice as you scribble away, your words a mess. But even so, you press on, crafting a message you toss out to sea. Just to see ...

Devoured by depression.

The words thunder through you, wreaking havoc in your head and your heart, but somehow you sense there's a way to beat the storm. You have never admitted the words before, so you grab the collection of glass and decide to pour it all out. The fragments land like rubble, remnants of the deception, deceit and lies that have cut into you for years. And while you desperately want to clear them away, you know that they are still pieces of you.

And that's when you notice the slivers of light, their figures stretching across the floor. Your fingers begin moving independently, collecting and arranging the pieces in a glittering spread, each a reminder of everyone who's left. Of the hurt you've felt, have held inside, and all of the tears you've inevitably cried. Do you deserve them?

The rays ripple in through the pane, ebbing over the shimmering display in a way you've never seen before: vivid, lucent, *scintillating.* The word hints at something more, gives you a sliver of—do you dare call hope?—that even when shattered, you can still give off light. While you can't piece together all the broken glass, you can at least learn to move on from the past. Make amends with their ghosts for the wrong that you've done, and use their pieces to make yourself whole, make yourself one.

Vina Nguyen

Eat

Content warning: eating disorder, child abuse, drug abuse, suicidal thoughts

A sharp crinkling and crunching woke me from a light sleep. Something like cellophane and wheat crackers. I thought of a family of raccoons rummaging through the garbage, whiskers askew, crumbs sticking to their faces.

Instead, I found her. Every time. Sneaking chips from the cupboard at 3 a.m. She jolted when I appeared, looking down at her elfish frame crouched on the kitchen lino, her upper body disappearing inside the cupboard.

Sheepishly, she rolled the bag shut. Snapped an elastic thrice around it and shoved it to the back of the deep cupboard. I'd bought that bag of chips from the convenience store that evening on my way home from school. An unopened, extra-large bag of my favourite salt and vinegar chips, now the size of an empty toilet paper roll. I pursed my lips.

She cleared her throat while filling a cup with water. "Those are so salty."

"It does say 'Salt 'n' Vinegar'," I said.

"I didn't have dinner," she pleaded.

"You choose not to have dinner, every day."

My mom pinched her tiny bulge of tummy fat and sighed.

"I've told you a thousand times. You're not fat." I snatched the bag of chips and turned on a heel.

"No!" she shrieked, yanking on my shirt. Neither of us had control, and it killed her, knowing whose behaviour I'd learned to mimic.

I devoured the rest of the chips in 83 seconds with my bedroom door locked and the window wide open. Then I quietly pulled out another bag—ketchup flavoured, my true favourite—that I'd kept in my backpack, cloaked in a towel, hidden behind a wall of shoeboxes and pushed deep into the darkest corner of my closet. I licked it clean in 5 minutes and 23 seconds. Then, as I cried, I pushed through 220 sit-ups and 65 push-ups and planked for 45 seconds x 3. Cool air pooled into the room as I lay collapsed on the floor, feeling the salt of my tears and sweat crust on my skin.

Teeth dreams haunted me. The bottom row always went first. My jaws seized and scissored against one another, misaligned and grating horribly. Whenever I yearned to speak, my lips protruded into sand-coloured shells and the hinges of my mouth clenched so tightly that my teeth shattered, popping like snipered glass windows.

Was it not having teeth that stopped me from speaking in my dreams? Or was it an excuse for avoiding a deeper, lingering fear—that if I did speak, the loss would be far more catastrophic than simply losing teeth? I began to worry that my dreams would invade reality one day, that I'd find myself wanting to speak but be unable to, because I'd obstructed the words for so long that I'd forgotten them. Forgotten the words that were so important to me—and so powerful that they could destroy everything I had.

Right before my body plumped into the shapeliness of a gourd, I got braces. For 7 years, after lunch and dinner, I weaved the floss around every bracketed tooth. Brushed at the beginning, middle, and end of each day—first with the regular orthodontic brush and then with the tiny pinetree brush. I devoted 1.5 hours a day to my teeth while other teenagers shared their first kiss, smacked gum against their lips and smiled without hooks grappling onto their cheeks. Yet, I couldn't put the toothbrush down, couldn't let go of flossing for one day.

Tightening, the other ritual. Once a month, right when the ache in my roots had subsided, the technician swung the pick and pliers in her hands like a plumber with a wrench. As she worked the brackets and wires and elastics on my teeth—cranking, cinching—a fire glowed in her eyes. I'd jump when a bracket snapped off, but she'd chuckle. The loose wire stabbed my gums, while saliva trickled down to my earlobe. My head waited to pop like a heated kernel.

I chuckled the first few times, coming home to a meal of salad rolls—the crunchy lettuce, chewy rice paper, tough pork and undercooked vermicelli—thinking it'd slipped my mom's mind that I'd had a tightening appointment. Except, it happened every fucking time. Imagine having to hoist a sack of rice onto a dislocated shoulder or bite with the sensitivity of skin instead of the dullness of teeth; I wanted to rip my jaws out because of the pain. Instead, I used scissors, snipping each bite right against my lips, which stoked the gleam in her eyes, until she exploded into a fit of laughter, cackling and rolling across the lino, gasping for air. I choked on each bite; each word I couldn't speak packed my mouth to the brim.

Maybe the teeth hauntings began that day, when it was 33 degrees Celsius and the AC whirred dizzily. My skin clung to the chair. I was in the middle of my seven-year-long treatment, and Mom had just fought with my orthodontist, threatening to take me to a better one. It was an empty threat—she didn't have the money. The orthodontist leaned me back, farther than usual, and if I wasn't so sticky, I'd have plunged headfirst into the ground. He said, "Look at these exposed roots. *Tsk. Tsk.* We're moving too fast. Your teeth might just fall right out."

The food didn't even taste good. Or more like, I couldn't taste it at all. Spring rolls, garlic bread, moon cake, pizza, fried rice, ice cream, and frozen durian all went down my throat as though I was hypnotized. I'd crave it like a coke addict, but the hit never came. Sometimes I sweated buckets as I stuffed and swallowed, but there was no stopping till there was nothing left in the house, till the numbness was gone or till exhaustion broke me.

I always ate quickly. The haste was strange. And I didn't want her to catch me in the act—the shameful, humiliating crouched position that I too often caught her in. Afterward, I'd go straight to the store and buy the same tray of muffins or bucket of chicken to make it appear like nothing had ever been gone.

Then, one Sunday afternoon, she bought two hefty Black Forest cakes from Safeway because they were on sale. She eyed me as she left to satiate her shoe obsession, leaving me behind with the cakes. Mental images of myself forcing down cake like a frenzied, rabid animal branded the indignity of my lack of control, weak character, and unrelenting urges to self-destruct with a sizzling iron deep into my chest. My lungs hyperinflated from the pain then became stuck. Full of stale, suffocating air. I threw open the back door. I wanted it all to stop, to go away, for it to disappear or for me to disappear. I hoisted a cake onto my palm, ready to pitch it deep into the backyard—but what would I do with the emptiness? The quiet in my mind? I didn't know who I was without this disorder.

As I chugged mouthfuls of cake, I recalled her disapproving eyes behind me in the mirror that morning, examining how tightly the jeans had hugged my thighs, and the question silenced me: did she consider how she'd judge me as she bought the cakes? A black hole was engulfing me from the inside, and suddenly, I envisioned myself lying flat on the carpet with wide black eyes, alone, choked dead from food.

She returned in 17 minutes. Didn't even make it to the mall. Took one look at me sitting cross-legged on the carpet in front of the TV, cradling a half-finished cake in my lap, and she screamed, stomped over, yanked it away. "Do the stairs. Now!" And I did. Without a word. Up and down, up and down … like my weight. But I looked *normal*. I looked *healthy*.

I checked the fridge before bed. Sure enough, she'd eaten the remaining cake and a half, and everything else. My jaw began clenching, as I knew that a vacant fridge foretold another emptiness. I crept down the hallway and touched an ear to her door: her weeping, straining against each sit-up, push-up and plank, and the *ssh-ssh* of my teeth sanding themselves down.

She squatted on the pool deck, timing my 40 laps. As I touched the wall and flipped, she yelled, "27 seconds! Too slow." Two more lengths and I was back at her feet. "29! Faster-faster!"

But I was never fast enough. She'd taught me there was no such thing as moderation. If you weren't fast, then you'd stopped. Lost. Failed. Dead.

"31."

"38."

"45."

My arms became wooden boards, my legs steel bars, my lungs fire. Were we born with different internal clocks from everyone else? Why were we racing to the end?

I could never swim fast enough, speak fast enough, eat fast enough or grow up fast enough.

The times I trained without her were my worst lap times, but my best swims. No shark chased me through the water. I was alone, protected.

Past midnight, I stepped off the bus and turned the corner and saw the lights still blazing on at the house. Ignoring my greeting, she resumed her other activities: scrubbing the stairs, lino, counters and stove top and bleaching the dishes, sinks and bathroom, as she did every day. I drifted off to sleep only to jerk awake moments later from the slap of a switch and warmth snatched from my body.

She gripped my blanket in one hand. "Go brush your teeth."

"What?" I murmured.

"Brush your teeth!"

"I did."

"Don't you *lie* to me. Get up."

"I've got midterms tomorrow. Leave me alone." I rolled over, but she dragged me by the wrist onto the floor.

"You want them to rot? You want to lose everything?"

I jumped to my feet. Spit flew and veins popped. Her tears brought tears to my eyes the way her guilt and shame had passed onto me. We couldn't be together. I thought of throwing myself out the open window, to escape from this, but instead I heard myself saying, "I'm not you." Clarity struck me as the words finally formed against the solidness of my teeth. But I broke her. My mom bolted down the hallway. And I closed the door between us.

"You don't have a scale in your bathroom," she says. She has shrunk since the last time I saw her, maybe three years ago. She's shrunk the way a plum dries into a prune. In every dimension—height, width, depth—my mom's losing against time, still.

She goes through my fridge, impressed by the bounty of vegetables, then frowns at the juice cartons. "Twenty-eight grams of sugar per serving—horrible for your teeth. Do you want diabetes?"

I stare. I've forgotten all about this. "Those've been there for over a week," I say.

She's surprised, maybe skeptical too. "Look at you, you should eat more—not too much—and you're still swimming? How many laps? How fast—" I've forgotten all about this.

Her eyes flit over to the cookies on the table again, and with slight unease, she creeps closer to them. I left them out to remind myself to eat them before they expired, but now I realize my mistake.

I pass her a small plate. "Why don't you have one?"

"One," she repeats, then tries to nibble slowly.

I trudge to the window, slide it open. The soft crunching fades behind me as I shut my eyes, again, trying to forget.

Kailash Srinivasan
Ma

Content warning: sexual assault

I turn fourteen the day my father dies and my mother falls into conversation with a man from our village who sings at local weddings, a man more bones than meat.

When my father was alive, my mother had two big complaints: one, he didn't have the means to buy a two-wheeler, and two, he never took her to the cinema. But Raju, the singer, owns a *pista*-green, second-hand Bajaj scooter, and every weekend he takes my mother and me to the movies, where we eat two samosas each. I love sitting in the dark, looking at the light from the screen illuminating the faces of people; the scent of deep-fried peas and *aloo* hanging in the air.

Once, I was in the cinema washroom next to a man whose cardigan wouldn't meet in the centre. He looked at me, then pushed his salty finger in my mouth. I wasn't sure what was expected of me, so I didn't tell anyone.

Even in the darkness of the cinema hall, I can see Raju and my mother holding hands. She's leaning her head on his chest. His fingers creep around her waist, pinch her stomach; discomfort runs up and down my skin, like a cockroach. On our way back, I am in the front, standing with my knees bent, so I don't block his vision, while he sings for her movie songs in the voices of popular playback singers: Rafi, Kishore.

Neighbours pull me into their homes, feed me leftover *kheer*, which makes the corners of my mouth and my fingers sticky, and ask me about my mother and her new lover.

"So soon? Are they ... together-together?"

"Not even married?"

"Didn't your father just die, Ram-Ram!"

"You must be ashamed."

"No regard for our culture, customs. *Tch-tch*."

I listen silently, nod politely, then cry on my way out.

Raju wakes at seven every morning to do *riyaz* on his harmonium. My mother orbits him, *Want more chai? Want hot water for your throat?* I have never seen her like this. She hums songs all day, applies rose perfume, decorates her hair with jasmine flowers, wears make-up.

She demands I learn to sing from him.

"Who is your favourite singer?" Raju asks.

"I *love* Kumar Sanu," I say without blinking.

"Oh! He's the easiest to copy. Just use your nasal voice and add a reverb at the end of every line. Like this—" His voice, mannerisms, expressions transform him to sound like Sanu. It impresses me so much, I want to embrace him. Yet I don't. My dead father would want at least one of us to remain loyal to him.

"Teach me, teach me," I beg, and my mother, overcome with affection, wets my face with kisses.

I begin waking up and practising before leaving for school. My mother buys me used cassettes of Kumar Sanu that sometimes make a screeching sound in the middle of a song.

For dinner Ma makes spinach *dal* and rice. Later, in bed, he plays with her fingers, rubs them one by one. As always, I pretend to be asleep, eyes half-closed, don't even swallow when my mouth goes dry. She must have shaken her head, because I hear her *jhumkas* bounce.

"Ali will wake up," she whispers at his attempts to unhook her sari blouse. For over a week I have heard them argue about whether I should be sleeping with them, like I always have with my parents, or in the living room, like a grown-up. Raju sighs loudly; the heat of his breath is on my neck. He tucks his palms under his head. In a few minutes my mother reaches over. She wants to be discreet, but the dancing glass bangles on her wrist give her away. They slip out of the room; their departed bodies leaving the bed weightless. I hear the closing of the bathroom door. The hinges need oiling. Her anklets jingle for several minutes, then they stop.

A few days before my fifteenth birthday, my mother and Raju are getting ready to go somewhere. She's wearing her gold necklace, her peacock-shaped earrings, and her favourite green sari with a red border: the one I picked for her two years ago.

I wait at the door, watching them ride away. Usually she forgets things—her handbag, comb—and returns to get them. But there's no sign of the scooter. This thrills me as desire dances below my belly.

I hurry to my mother's bedroom to do what I love the most: raiding her dresser. Sitting in front of the long mirror, I apply her pink lipstick. My lips come alive. I pout and kiss my hands, trace the outline, the indents where the colour hasn't touched. Her *jhumkas* hang heavily from my ears. I feel soft, feminine, desirable.

When I hear the *tut-tut* of Raju's scooter, I wipe my face roughly with Ma's handkerchief and push it far inside the dustbin. My mother is glowing, long strings of jasmine flowers hang from her hair. She presses her made-up cheeks against mine and announces, "We're married." Raju kisses her, shoving his tongue in her mouth. He looks at me as he does this.

That night my mother tells me to move to the living room. When I protest, Raju takes me aside. His lips smile, yet his grip on my wrist is iron-like.

"Listen," he hisses, "there's an old man who roams after dark and snatches children who sleep in their parents' bed. Want me to call him?"

I shake my head.

"Good boy."

He goes inside, and my mother bolts her bedroom door. I pull the sheet to my chin, wait for her in the dark, wait for her to come and get me, but the door remains closed.

"Ma," I whisper.

Raju gets the extra *roti*, the last piece of chicken, all of my mother's love.

"Your father is singing at a big wedding next week," she gushes one morning. "They even gave him an advance. Tell him, Papa."

She had started calling him that, as a way to encourage me to do so.

Raju closes the harmonium, pushes it away.

"Is everything okay, Papa?" she asks.

He runs his palm over his face. "They hired this new singer, Gopa, and asked me to return the money. But they told me we were still welcome to attend the wedding."

Ma curses Gopa—wishing for him to lose his voice or get electrocuted by the microphone. "Then everyone will realize," she says, "that there's no one better than you."

We go to the wedding anyway. Nothing bad happens to Gopa. His honeydew voice travels out of the large speakers. Usually at weddings, guests scurry to the food stalls, burdening their small plates with too much food. But no one leaves their uncomfortable chairs. Even the children are quiet, fascinated by the short man on stage. His pencil-thin moustache looks like it's been drawn on.

When the song ends, the audience goes crazy, clapping louder and louder, louder than any applause I've ever heard. Raju chews his food angrily.

"Once more," they scream, "once more."

Later, as I'm serving food onto my plate, I sense someone standing close to me. It's Gopa, his sharp chin and neatly pressed grey safari suit making him look like a movie star. I notice his pink cheeks, eye shadow and liner. Was that a hint of lipstick?

"You were really good." I try not to sound too eager.

"Thanks." He smiles and I can't explain the tingle at the back of my neck.

"Do you want to sit together?"

We occupy an empty table. Gopa tells me how he came into the profession: through a friend who knew a friend who knew a friend. Hearing him talk, seeing his lips—I wonder if they are soft—a hot flush touches my cheeks.

There are questions later. What was I doing with Gopa? Don't I know he is the reason Raju lost the gig? What was he saying?

"We were just talking," I say.

A few days later, I fall asleep while listening to the cassette Gopa gave me, lost in the sweetness of his voice. A sound makes me open my eyes; it's the middle of the night. Raju and my mother are by my bedside, which is nothing more than a thin sheet on top of a straw mat. The cassette player is still on. My mother yanks the plug out of the point and slams it against the wall.

"He's smitten, your boy." Raju strikes the tape recorder with his foot. "He likes boys."

My eyes are downcast. I don't understand why I feel such shame.

"Look at him, he can't even meet our eyes." Raju is not done; he maniacally pulls the spool out of the tape.

My mother withdraws her gaze from Raju, from me. Stares at the floor. Her not saying anything frightens me more. I'm crying, and I don't know why. "Ma," I say.

"Quiet, you don't have a mother, your mother is dead."

Her words close in around me, and I am clutching her feet, crying. "I am sorry, I am sorry," I say. She tries to free her leg, and I hold on to her rubber slipper. When she and Raju go back to their room, I am still on the floor, hugging her slipper.

That night I leave home with some money I have saved and wait at the bus depot. At first light, I take the bus to the neighbouring town, to the town where Gopa lives. I wake up in the late afternoon to a baby's loud cry. The child's mother loosens the buttons of her cotton blouse, and its tiny, wet mouth curls around her dark nipple.

I get off at the last stop and ask around for directions to the Mankameshwar Temple. Someone points toward the slums— hundreds of huts packed tightly together—below the bridge. The smell of burning coal, cheap soap and desperation. A boy, much younger than I, has a bag full of plastic bottles slung over his shoulder. He wants to know if I'm lost. His eyes light up on hearing Gopa's name.

"I'll take you."

It is early evening. The sky is a giant grey beard. There is hardly any room to walk. A naked boy wearing only a black thread around his waist crouches as another boy works the water hand pump. He is also naked. Inside the tiny one-room mud homes, women squat in front of *chulhas*, boiling gruel or making *rotis*.

Gopa's thatched hut has a thin curtain for a door. I step around the sewage water. Gopa looks up at me and nods. He doesn't ask me any questions and goes back to his harmonium.

After we put the dinner plates away, we share a cigarette, my first. I can hear hens clucking outside, the smell of food being cooked in the homes floating in the air. A drunkard wails an old *ghazal* about a woman gently tucking her arm into the crook of her lover's arm and taking him home. Someone beats a child, the striking of a calloused palm against tender skin.

"You have done nothing wrong," says Gopa. I haven't told him anything yet. "Mothers are not always the most selfless."

He sprawls on a thin sheet, uses his arms as a pillow. Sleep, when it finally comes, is deep and restful. The sound of boiling tea rouses me in the morning. Gopa brings two glasses; I close my fingers around mine and drink deeply.

I will not see or speak to my mother for a year. I'll hear from a friend that she's pregnant, that it's most likely a boy. I'll share the stage many times with Gopa; get propositioned by mothers looking for a husband for their daughters; be cornered by drunk married men who'll want me to blow them. They will call me names when I refuse.

This will also be the year I'll kiss Gopa in a cold hotel room. I'll climb onto the bed with him, feel the heat of his body on mine, smell the warm, damp, adult air; and afterward feel what I did was wrong, dirty, immoral. It will be the year I'll realize it is okay if a boy likes another boy, it is okay to feel the way I feel.

The next time I'll see my mother, I'll be performing at a politician's wedding. She'll be twice her normal size; her hand will reach instinctively over her belly.

There will be hundreds of people in shiny clothes and shiny shoes; a young stage dancer will dance to a Bhojpuri song while men grope her.

The tables laid out on the lawn will be piled with food. I'll be in a cream-coloured safari suit; the blinding spotlights will be on my face. I'll spot my mother among those people, and tears will sting my eyes. She will hear my voice, but will continue eating, not even look my way.

Guests will be dancing and flinging money that will fall all around me: fifties, hundreds, five-hundreds. From up here, everyone will seem happy. Drinks in their hands, songs on their lips, they will repeat after me. Guests will come up to me after the performance to shake my hand, hug me, stand too close, tell me over and over again how happy I make them.

I will see my mother by the chairs at the far end of the lawn. She'll glance up at me and look away, like I'm a stranger, not her son. I will want to talk to her, ask her if she ever loved me, but

Gopa will grab my arm and shake his head. His cheeks will be wet.

I'll go back to the hotel with Gopa, and all night he'll hold me as I cry for Ma, for what I have lost. He'll hum the same song Ma used to sing to me: *You're my moon, you're my sun, you're the star of my eyes; I live for you, you're a beautiful dream of mine.*

Robin van Eck
No One Tells You

Emergency c-section. Heart rate dropping with each contraction. Not dilating. Need to get this baby out now. You never once worried that anything like this might happen. Thought doctors knew what they were doing.

You hold the bundle in your arms, unsure, confused. Foreign. Alien. This thing came out of you. What now?

No one tells you because they don't know either.

Naps will be unheard of but mandatory. Stop to brush your teeth, pull a comb through your mass of knotted hair. A haircut might be in your future.

Throughout the year in day homes, daycares and schools, pediculosis (head lice) are not uncommon as children are in close contact with each other. We are constantly informed of cases of lice and would like to remind parents of the procedures for treating head lice. Please see attached information.

A sigh. A curse. Not again.

Wash the hair, comb, watch the little friggers tantrum and spasm because of a loss of blood. Their frantic legs grasp at the air, searching for something to latch onto. Flush them. Garbage them. Anywhere but here.

A bruise on her back. Seemingly from nowhere.

It doesn't hurt much, she promises.

You watch it grow, expand. And then another on her leg. Her arms.

What did you do to yourself?

Her eyes fill with tears. You're mad at me.

Not mad. Is someone hurting you?

She shakes her head.

You lay together in her bed, reading a story, talking about the day. Mental note, when you're alone, consult Google.

Google says anyone who has hair can get head lice. They're not caused by being dirty. Head lice don't cause illness or disease. They're spread by touching heads with someone who has it or by sharing hats, hairbrushes and combs. If one person in the family has it, it's likely someone else does too. Check the whole crew. Check every week. *See detection combing*.

These tiny insects can cause a lot of stress and a lot of work.

Head lice do not appear out of thin air or from the ground. They are human parasites that have been around since the beginning of time. If they can't survive without human blood, they must be a part of us, all of the time.

The doctor's office is quiet. Only the soft hum of the lights, the phone ringing.

What brings you in today? The nurse doesn't smile. Is this how they are trained? Emotionless. Disconnected.

Show me, the doctor says.

She lifts her shirt. The bruises have multiplied.

A sheet full of tests that you don't understand, but the significance is loud, hostile. Gut punch.

Detection combing. An organized way to look for lice and nits from the scalp down.

Will need a fine-toothed comb. Paper towel. And a fuck-ton of patience. No swearing. No freaking out.

Be methodic. Precise.

Better to do it when hair is wet.

Proceed to weekly check-ins if no lice are found.

If lice found, skip to method for destroying the creepy bastards.

The hospital bed is hard, the sheets thin.

Heads together, you lay and talk while she sleeps because you can't handle hearing her gentle breaths, for fear that they will stop.

The bag on the pole administers a steady stream of medication. It should fight off the infection, but this one has burrowed too deep, clinging hard to her insides.

She will be here a while.

Late nights seemed hard. Cold cloths to subdue a fever, up and down changing buckets. Headaches. Stomach-aches.

This is harder.

What did she do to deserve this? Was it the vaccinations? There's no history in the family. Why her?

The shampoo, cream, rinse, whatever you choose, will kill the live lice and may or may not kill the nits. The smell of essential oils course through the house. Suffocating the rooms as much as the bugs clinging for life to the shafts of hair.

Nits don't have to be removed,

Really? They don't need to be removed?

but you may choose to comb them out.

That's a lot of extra work.

Read the fine print: *A second treatment is almost always needed.*

After a week her hair begins to fall out. First a few strands and then bigger clumps. Bald patches reveal dry skin that didn't exist before.

She sits up and smiles, admiring herself in the mirror.

You miss the braids, the ponytails, the excessive cries of stop pulling my hair.

I have a flat spot on the back of my head, she says.

You should have given her more tummy time. Does that make you a bad parent? Like the time she went to school with no hat or mitts—no snow pants—and the temperature dipped to minus 22 degrees Celsius. Or her lunches consisted of a juice box and bag of crackers.

It's okay. She pulls a toque down, over her ears. Hats are cool. Her voice is weak, fragile.

You must keep it together. For her. For you.

You strip the beds and pillowcases. Gather the laundry. Everything the hair may have touched. Wash it. Burn it. Kill it.

Load by load, up and down the stairs until you're tired and the water bill is on the verge of exploding, but the bugs will be gone in the gurgle and splash of the rinse cycle draining and refilling. Spin the shit out of them.

Vacuum. Wash down all surfaces. It might be overkill, but what else is there to do. Feel important. Doing the parental thing. Make sure no one else catches them. The inconvenience. The fatigue.

Now boil the brushes, the combs, the hair ties and clips.

Are the other parents doing their part? Are they working as hard as you to ensure it doesn't keep spreading?

No hugging. No sharing hats. No selfies. Not a warning or suggestion. A demand.

This is what you can do.

That, and weekly check-ins, until the comb comes out clean.

Her energy returns, colour splashes across her cheeks. It's a miracle. A sigh of relief. You've been clenching parts of your body you didn't know could clench. Finally, she can come home. There's nothing left to do but rest.

You read one story after another for no other reason than to hear the sound of your voice and to feel her beside you, dozing gently, her hand resting on your arm. An extension of you. That moment, in birth when she was so foreign, has transformed into something greater. When you couldn't imagine life with her, now you can't imagine life without her.

Eventually, her hair will grow back.

Rayanne Haines

Ledges

in the silence of
wheat fields behind
my parents' house,
i made plans for
who i would marry,
the sons & daughters
i would birth, ways of   escaping
my farming town.   all this
before the internet,
when the world lay
small at my feet
and i knew   nothing
of women oceans away.
Before my breasts had
grown and i had to worry
about things   like shame.
Before I knew of women
hanging from windows
looking for ledges.

Nadeen Almubarak

A Story of Revenge

Content warning: sexual assault
Today, I kill my husband.

I sip on blonde coffee in one of the little traditional cups and listen to my grandma chant about my dead mother and how I'll never have her heart. She never mentions my husband. Your mother was a perfect child, she says, never cried, never fussed, never complained, and she always did what I told her without a word. I sip and nod.

When my daughter cries from the corner of the room, my grandmother chides her. Stop crying, child, what are you on about now, she says. What you're doing to your mama is *haram*, look how tired she is. She's teething, *habibti*, I say to my grandma before picking up my daughter. Bring her to me, she says, stretching her arms. Then she kisses her forehead, puts a thin finger in my daughter's mouth to bite on, wraps a fallen hijab around the child and rocks her back-and-forth until they both fall asleep—all without mention of my husband.

I've always blurred the lines between fiction and reality, bending and stretching events to fit with my preferred perception, living on the borderline between the two. When my mother died, I wove tales of wild abandonment, and when my father remarried, I imagined her ghost flitting about to celebrate the completion of my desertion; why else would she leave? When my family did not allow me to see her after she died, reciting that *honouring the dead is burying them as fast as possible*, I imagined an infernal abyss that only I could assuage. Months later, I would shake with cries for a need I could not name, then I'd slap my cousins across the face and hide behind my grandma's body—a frail shelter from my aunts' admonishments—and relish in the defensive tone of the excuses she made for my actions. It sounded like love. Your aunts are cruel, she would say to me later as she braided my hair before bed, so you have to be on your best behaviour around them.

The day I met my husband, two years ago, I twisted my indiscretion into a love story between a teenager and a college boy. Unlike fiction, however, it did not end with a happily ever after. We agreed to take a ride in the car one day, a romantic drive along the corniche. Later that night, after returning from the hospital, my grandmother cried. Why would you do this, I raised you right, she said. When I flinched, she exposed my arm and found my skin adorned with blue and purple bruises. She trembled in her place for a few seconds, her eyes brimming with tears. Oh, oh, oh, she muttered. Then she pointed to a faded scar on her upper arm and hugged me gently.

That night, I lay in my grandma's bed after she tucked me in and couldn't make sense of my love story, even as dawn slithered across the sky and birds twittered in the morning light. I thought of a courageous girl who pushed the boundaries of the acceptable in the country to see her love, but I could make no sense of why I felt betrayed by the boy. Hadn't I willingly met with him?

My grandmother snored lightly and I thought of my wedding day, merely a week after I had confirmed I'd been pregnant. Thank God he agreed to take you as a wife, one of my seven aunts had said—I can't remember which; they all sound the same. Whenever I write a story that involves them in my head, they merge into one aunt.

I only wanted to see him, I told my grandma, who said that I shouldn't have, then kissed my forehead and said boys don't understand what girls want. They think that giving their eyes access to your face is giving them access to everything.

Access. Such a strange word.

This will spoil my life, I protested on my wedding day. I shan't recover. Quiet child, an aunt said. This is the only way to give you cover.

Is it really? I asked my grandma.

It's for your own protection, my girl, she said.

I know it was bad to speak to him. I know I'm bad.

If there is anything I'm certain about, she said, it is your goodness.

She's not a child anymore, Mother, another aunt said. She's brought nothing but shame to this family. She is a disgrace. Ah, if only your mother could know. She would sob until her tears filled this room.

I decided that day that my mother might be better able to love me from death. Perhaps, if she were alive, her love wouldn't fit me. Perhaps, in her abandonment of me, I have found the greatest tool to self-destruct, and that is my destiny: to become a person who wonders, always, *Who am I, and what am I doing here? And how do I unbecome?*

Mama, I whispered to my grandma before my new husband hauled me into the bridal suite. Doesn't a marriage license give him *unlimited access*? Go in, she said. Then she turned around and walked away.

That night, the violation reoccurred. And every night after that. I was wooed by his dark hair and dimpled cheeks, but a violent revulsion erupted from deep within my stomach every time he entered the room, even when he whispered words of love to me. I wondered if he really loved me, if the love story I'd invented was still alive in him.

I lay beside him afterward, trying to think of words for Chapter Two of this new fable, but I failed. And that hurt. That was the first time I lost my ability to story an event, lost my voice, myself. I agonized over that all night. *Why has my life become ordinary?* I beat my stomach in a fit of fury, hoping my baby would die, convincing myself I would be saving it from this filthy world. Then, like the neurotic that I am, I hugged my stomach and whispered sweet words to my child.

For the next two years, my husband and I established a rhythm, an organic performance in which he played the role of Majnun and I Layla, a necessary façade in the face of insurmountable fear and obligations. Loneliness and violation disturbed me, and no matter how much I tried to be happy, my melancholy crept in, and I had no choice but to fall between the creases of self-blame and set up a lodging there. Even my beautiful daughter's face couldn't pluck me out, nor my grandma's hate for my husband. Until, that is, she had an idea one day.

You could kill him, she said. I snickered and looked away.

You should, she said. They'd know, I replied. No, honouring the dead is burying them as fast as possible, she said. No autopsy, no proof. I'll give you a mix of nutmeg, saffron and chamomile; that will be enough to knock out a horse, then you can do it.

For weeks after, I considered what my grandmother had said. No, I thought. I would never do that. But then he'd pick up my daughter and I'd feel a restricted panic seep through my body, and the coarse realization that my baby was not safe with her father would freeze my heart. I have not enough flesh, bones or body to protect her. Oh, if only hate was enough to form a forcefield around the two of us.

In those moments, I created the perfect story of revenge, one the opposite of self-hate, and I decided I would end it with my own hands.

I refill my cup with the blonde coffee and feel large, larger than the earth and the universe, larger than my childhood and my dreams, larger than my desires and fears and futile life, than my own abilities and others' capabilities. I feel infinite and cold. A little while later, my grandma opens an eye—a single eye—and looks at my child before shifting her gaze to me. Is he sleeping yet? she asks. I nod.

You have access now, she whispers.

Heidi Klaassen

The Anvil

Nonfiction

There is a photo of her uterus on her cell phone. The surgeon didn't hesitate when asked to take the picture—an understanding between two women. Three hours into recovery, the doctor appeared in her hospital room, eager to airdrop the image. The gynaecologist had posed it, she said, on a background of blue surgical paper, the fallopian tubes raised in victory, symbolic of what they both hoped would mean an end to the patient's chronic pelvic pain. The ugliness of hurt betrayed the beautiful chrysalides that had formed there. She reasoned this was the price to pay for three successful pregnancies, three incredible boys, three unwanted but necessary caesarean sections.

It's a surreal paradox, to be willing to lose a part of herself with the hope of also losing an elusive and sinister thief: pain. It germinates in the body but ripens in the soul. Chronic pain violates, the degradation an allegory for the larger collective female hurt. Eradicating it risks losing so much. A splintered decision to also give up a part of herself.

She is made to endure pain, she has heard. Childbirth, by any means, is the agonizing necessity of sowing seeds. Years of debilitating lunar cycles are the rightful preparations for this process. Pain is life. Pain is woman's inevitability. Pain is the result of behaviour. Pain is our fault, in all its incarnations.

The light starts to go out in her eyes when the pain wraps around her like an unwanted advance from a stranger. The vicinity of its burn unravels the complexities of its trigger. It's heavy inside her, an anvil. It reminds and degrades. She tries to pull away, slap it across the face, but it persists, shameless, groping under her skirt. She wants to ignore it. It follows her, a shadow looming. Nobody else sees it. They don't understand why she withdraws. She learns that she is to withstand this pain, even question its existence, because it can't be seen. All tests come back negative. This is a good thing, they say. She should be smiling! She should probably just go home and get some rest. Take some ibuprofen. She's a busy mom. Get some rest.

The pain snags. It stops her legs from running. Rusty hands on a clock. Her stomach learns to fear food, afraid of unbolting the door and letting an unknown enemy into an already violent household. Every twenty-eight days, its anger grows, unleashing rage over her fetal form, clutching the heating pad that has permanently scarred her skin. The burn from the heat obscures the pain. It tricks the brain. A trade-off. She screams inside a bubble that, from the outside, looks like a mom of three, an entrepreneur, an artist and a wife. Touch is repellant, an enemy with the face of a man she has loved for twenty-one years.

Suggestions are made; reasons, conditions she realizes women are dealing with all over the world, sharing her silence and her shame. New hurt she's never heard of in the grand speculum of things. Debilitating yet invisible causes with names like endometriosis, adenomyosis and polycystic ovarian syndrome. Don't worry, they say. These things aren't deadly; they just eat up your quality of life, follow you, stalk and grope; interfere with relationships, mental health. She learns a new term: invisible disability. Unwanted advances from these predators happen without warning or apology. Complaints are seen as exaggeration and hypochondria, visits to the emergency room interpreted as drug-seeking performances. After all, pain experienced by women is a major symptom of a widespread condition: hysteria. Take some ibuprofen. Get some rest. Follow up if the pain persists. *But I* am *following up. It* has *persisted. Over a year now, every day ...*

Pain? Still? Every. Day. That's what chronic means. Its rough hand, violating and penetrating through a pair of jeans. She can no longer wear jeans. She starts wearing only loose clothing to placate its fury—or is it hers? She throws the fork across the counter and it slides into her favourite vintage butter dish, chipping it.

I thought you loved that butter dish, Mom? It's broken now too.

Mind over matter, she reasons. Surely, this predator can be pushed away by sheer force of will. But it thrusts into her, feeds on her fear and isolation, whispering, *Nobody will believe you. They can't see it. You don't want everyone to know about that pain, do you?*

The first visit into the operating room feels hopeful. Results, evidence, justice. This will put an end to the violence. It doesn't. They can't find it. Elusive and insidious, stealthy despite the bright lights and expert interrogators.

Here's a prescription, they say. Medical management is all we can do for the pain until we find the cause. But she quit drinking eight years and two-hundred and twenty-seven days ago, so aren't these pills a dangerous trip to take in a body bent on sobriety? Are they sure the pain won't find her anyway? It will make her harder to find, they say. Does she want the pain with her every day? She takes the pills.

The blue ones are for nighttime. She learns that she has two hours before they will knock her out. It can't find her once that happens, not until morning. The white ones are for when she wakes up. If she sleeps in, it will have found her already. Pinning her down on a Saturday morning, the anvil. Don't fall behind with the meds. Stay ahead of the pain, they say.

The next doctor, a lady with sparkly pink shoes, offers an option: they can take away one of its hiding places. It could be in there, like a fugitive, reaching out with a dirty hand, grabbing and tearing. *You mean take away ... that place? But that's mine. It's sacred. My babies came from there. Won't I be old without it?* She thinks about the word, its ugly *hystory*. Do you want to face the pain every day? She signs the consent for surgery.

They take the organ and the lady doctor with the sparkly pink shoes airdrops the photo. A memento for an album that contains pieces of her that have been removed over the course of her life as a girl and a woman: trust, control, dignity, uterus.

Again, she is hopeful, but when the morphine wears off and the vomiting stops, it whispers in her ear again as she tries to resume normal: *I'm back, honey. Did you miss me?* Its tongue in her ear, nauseating, uncomfortable, disquieting. She doesn't want to tell anyone, disappoint them. How could it have her again? Even after the word that is only ever whispered: hysterectomy. It's another dirty secret, another burden she has brought about by the sole act of being female. *Mom, are you crying in there? I need to go pee.* She reapplies the mascara and opens the door. Hugging him makes her cry more.

Her pain seems mundane in its universality. Disease, child-birth, trauma, violence, shame. It's everywhere. It's invisible, hidden beneath acne and Botox, toques and hijabs, power suits and pasties. She learns about forums and groups that push back against the pain. Me too, they say, about a host of hurts that plague the female in a world where their importance is relatively new.

It's a long wait. The specialist has a line-up of women ahead of her. In the meantime, there's a pain clinic. They will help her to wait, she's told. The waiting hurts. *If the new doctor finds your pain, will you be able to ride bikes with us again?*

Months pass. Medicines are offered like salsa-filled paper cups at Costco: Cymbalta, Visanne, Lyrica, Morphine, Tramadol, Percocet, Naproxen, Tramacet, Orilissa, Amitriptyline ... These are the ones she remembers through the brain fog, nausea, weight gain, weight loss, blurred vision, dry mouth, itchy skin, memory loss, insomnia, drowsiness, heart palpitations, diarrhea, consti-pation, loss of appetite, swollen extremities, bone loss, mood swings, night sweats and hand tremors. She buys a pill dispenser with a section for each day of the week to help her keep track. She gets to know her pharmacist's kids' names and preferred sporting activities.

The day arrives and she feels like she has an appointment with God. He is a leader in pelvic pain and minimally invasive surgery, a hero. He tells her that, after six pelvic surgeries over her lifetime, beginning with a hernia repair at the age of five weeks, her nerves are now bound in scar tissue, unable to stop sending pain signals to her brain. Bound in scar tissue. She will literally have to lose her nerve. He can see her in a few months for the surgery he calls a 'Hail Mary'. Complicated and rare, it will involve cutting sections of two peripheral nerves from her right side. She will have a large numb spot. This is irreversible. Numb: the antisocial cousin of pain.

Through it all, she knows her good fortune. She is aware of how much worse it could be. This makes it harder. Who is she to complain? Who is she to put her family through this? She hates herself in a scalding bath, the water discolouring her skin to a slapped pink.

The recovery is jarring. Every nerve around the amputees take on the duties of their fallen comrades. At times, the sensations are unbearable. Equatorial sunburn mixed with funny bone lightening.

The contents of the orange bottles on the kitchen counter ebb and flow, their rattling sounds punctuating conversation in the house. *I hate your pain, Mom. I just want to punch it.* Me too.

As the healing gradually reveals relief, the need to be rid of the bottles of fog becomes evident. *Did the doctor take the mad away? Can you carry me to bed now?*

The first day without their chemical hug, she is brimming with panic. The bottles are moved into a cupboard, out of sight. She has a job interview in two weeks. The withdrawal has to be over by then. This job would mean something, a salvation, the reward for coming through whole after layers of herself have been peeled away by this beast with poisoned tentacles that erode everything within reach. The boys are forgetting how she was. *Remember when I used to laugh so hard I snorted?*

The second day is much worse. No sleep. The agitation and restless limbs, agony. When night arrives, it's filled with anxiety, sweat and disturbing dreams. Listless hours of an unsettled mood drift by.

Days of cognitive disrepair spiral her into sadness. She tries to speak, to write, but she has lost her words.

On day nine, she visits the pain clinic and speaks in simple terms. Her brain won't allow more. They tell her she should have tapered, taken a few weeks to wean off the pharmaceuticals. Enough time has been wasted, she says. Cold turkey. By day twelve, she can eat again without nausea. Colour in the world regains its brilliance. In the periphery, there is still fog. Her words are out there.

She goes back into the world. She's scared of being too hopeful. She's been burned before. She has the scars to prove it. Her words come back. She gets the job. She laughs, and the boys recognize her. The pain returns in tiny, creeping steps, on tiptoe. It's much weaker now, but there. Its flaccid arms reach out but can't always connect. She starts to run again. It hurts, but she's running. On the treadmill, she visualizes outrunning the predators—all of them.

The costs are high. Me too, women call. I felt that pain, I still do. It hurt me, he hurt me, they hurt me. It never goes away entirely. Time does not heal all wounds; they just turn into numb spots. It's irreversible. What remains moves her forward, wheels turning on bikes with her boys. The alternative is to stay in one place with the anvil.

Tristan Hay Lee

Wings and Legs

Content warning: infant fatality, suicide reference

When I was young, so young you'll say I couldn't remember, my sister snuck into our mother's room and sprayed herself with perfume. A shimmering mist hung in the air before she stepped through, and by the time it was my turn there was nothing left; just the smell of our mother and her inexplicable womanness. Her name was Wanda, which fit. My sister was Helen, which was a lot to live up to.

As we lay on our stomachs in the backyard, a blue butterfly landed on Helen's wrist. Flipping through a field guide years later, I learned it was called 'gossamer-winged'—a lady in a blue dress, with a shawl. Helen let it rest, as it opened and closed like the mouth of a flower, before she lifted it to her lips, bit off both its wings and swallowed them. She was ten years old.

A few months later, our parents dragged us to the butterfly conservatory where their sculpture was installed. This time we both wore my mother's perfume on our wrists. With envy I noticed that butterflies still swarmed Helen, despite the blood on her hands. Suddenly she was trembling at the sensation of their petunia-petal wings brushing against her skin. Sobs ricocheted throughout her body until, in one fluttering movement, the butterflies burst into flight.

Helen was mourning the one she had obliterated, the one she had taken into herself.

And I remember wondering, with my seven-year-old brain, who this repentant new sister was. I wondered when she had swapped places with the other Helen without me noticing.

A similar changeover happened last fall when I discovered my sister had left her baby in her car. I thought of the level-headed sister I had known—the one who called my mother to ask if she had refilled her precriptions, the one who alphabetized her spice drawer—and wondered where she had gone that day. I wondered if we would ever see her again.

And the answer, of course, was the answer to them all: no one, never, nowhere, no.

When I received the call, its connection to my sister felt strange and wrong. I learned the news through my father, which was a horrible thing to do to him. He took heart medication and had always loved children. He sounded like the calm before a storm, whereas I felt like the calm of dead wind. Limp branches. Stifling heat.

The truth is, at twenty-nine I was no longer close to Helen in the way we had been when we were children. She still sent yearly Christmas cards, but in the last five years, she had married, moved away from the city and become an expert supermarket shopper. Helen hadn't attended a single exhibition since leaving Toronto, even after our parents became notable for their abrading technique. Not even my debut last year.

"Could you pick us up?" my father asked.

I was in the middle of a day-long endeavour, developing prints in my darkroom. Ten minutes later, I cast a glance at the luminous figure on my shelf and was out the door, the submerged print now unsalvageable. An hour later I was outside my parents' apartment.

I blinked. They were dressed in clean starched collars and unscuffed shoes. My father wore an overcoat I had never seen before. They slipped into the back of the car like I was their chauffeur and refrained from telling me how late I was.

"You're wearing lipstick," I said. My mother clapped a clay-stained hand to her mouth like she had burned her tongue.

No one bothered mapping the route. I got us good and lost. The absence in the passenger seat unnerved me, and I wanted to ask why no one had sat up front.

"How did you hear?" I asked, to create noise.

"Mark," said my father. Husband.

"She wasn't even one," my mother said quietly. The absence of her name hung in the air, charged with electricity.

"Was he there?" I asked. "Mark?" Husband.

"No," my father said. "At work."

"They were coming from the hospital," my mother said. "I think he just didn't know what to do."

"Doesn't he have family?" Too petulant. I could sense my mother frowning.

"His parents are flying in from Montréal." Then, "She's your sister. She needs you."

"I just didn't think this is what it would take to see the inside of their house."

"Christmas in Cambridge doesn't make sense," my mother countered. "She's the only one out here. It's three against one."

"It's this weather," my father said, on a different planet. "No one expects a heatwave in the fall."

"Where did it happen?" I said. He didn't respond.

Eventually we began passing the familiar fields of corn and apple trees and livestock.

My station wagon squealed into their driveway, and we gazed at the impassive beige-brick house. It breathed like it was empty. My parents had a key, but we stood on the doorstep until Mark reached the door, giving him time to reassemble himself. He breathed like he was empty too.

She was upstairs, leaning against the radiator, strangely immobile.

"Helen?" I ventured. Her eyes leapt to mine and held. I wondered if, like me, she was remembering that morning fifteen years ago when I found her on our bathroom floor. Two sisters. Sworn to secrecy.

My mother helped her up, and we all averted our eyes. It was already beginning, the self-preservative process by which would avoid looking directly at her ever again. She emptied her purse on the sheepskin rug: empty sunglasses case, *Slaughterhouse Five* in near-perfect condition, sixty-five cents. Four receipts from Foodland. I don't know what she was expecting to find.

Slowly, the leaning shadows in the unlit room folded in the other direction and faded into themselves. Still no one said a word.

The police had told us someone needed to be with her at all times for at least forty-eight hours. I looked at her, with her luminous warm skin, inches away, drawing and exhaling breath, and wondered if we would ever see her again.

Eventually Helen cleared her throat and we all leaned toward her like she was a cool oasis in the desert.

"Groceries," she said. "In the car." My father and I met eyes and quickly looked away. I guess that's where it happened.

As we popped open the trunk, the stench of rotting food wafted out and poisoned our lungs. We emptied the bursting plastic bags, salvaging what we could. The meat had spoiled. The fruit was overripe. An entire tub of Breyers ice cream had turned to soup.

Local tragedies usually resulted in a trifecta of casseroles, carnations and unsolicited call-ins. My sister received none of these gifts except the dignity of absolute privacy. This is because there are a lot of mistakes that people can be generous about, but leaving your baby in a car is not one of them.

Helen's disappearance seemed natural, almost logical. By the forty-ninth hour, as we were driving back to the city, Mark called to say she was gone.

And in the months after she returned, I often caught my mother's burning eyes following Helen across a room, wondering how her first daughter had come to the conclusion that there was something redeemable here, something worth coming back to.

During her disappearance, Helen called me on the landline. I should have told her all the sensible things that an ordinary person would—*you can't leave Mark high and dry, come back and face yourself, people will talk*. And such. But ordinary was difficult when I could hear her breathing on the other end, like back when we'd exchange secrets in cupboards and closets, before she ripped out all her hair and locked herself in our bathroom. It was that stage of night when time becomes void, when you say things that never resurface. She told me her temptations, petty grudges, things she had been lying to herself about for years. What she didn't tell me was that this call was a process of self-extermination.

Out of nowhere she said, "There are these aliens in Vonnegut's books, Tralfamadorians. They don't see humans as two-legged. They see us as a kind of huge millipede—babies' legs on one end and old people's legs at the other." I was standing at the window, phone to ear, wondering if she was cocooned in the same pale moonlight.

"Why?" I asked.

"Because they see every moment of your life in one glance."

I closed my blinds. Darkness slatted in.

"You're so lucky," she said. "Just like Mom and Dad. You've never doubted for a minute that you're special."

"That's not true," I said in amazement.

"I'm just jealous," she said in her temperate voice. "Sometimes I just want to be little again. I hate this town. I hate going around cleaning things that just get soiled. I hate waking up knowing that I can count down the days or do nothing at all. And everyone here acts like it doesn't make them want to slit their wrists. I've thought things so awful you couldn't imagine. I …" Something cold entered my veins.

"Oh god," she breathed. "I've done something terrible."

When she came back, she was no longer my sister. In her place was a neurotic woman with twitchy, prosecuted eyes. She replaced Helen the same way a monarch emerges fully formed from the silk of a chrysalis. Along the way, she had racked up four thousand in credit card debt and lost almost fifteen pounds.

In the week following this metamorphosis, her husband often looked to me imploringly, as if I held the key to getting her back. He would call me when he found her sleeping in the bathtub, or when she returned from the supermarket with eighty-three pomegranates. I was in Cambridge so often, I started losing clients.

After a month of new Helen, she shattered Daughter II. Years ago, our parents had gifted each other to us in sculpture. They made a sister piece, Daughter I, which I kept in my apartment. I had Helen, she had me. That evening she smashed me on the kitchen floor so hard that shards went flying into the minestrone. Mark called for the last time.

I take her on errands. My parents pick alternate days. I bring her to my place and try to show her the darkroom, but my work still bores her as much as it used to. She ignores Daughter I on my shelf.

We were driving somewhere today, just the two of us, when suddenly Helen wanted out of the car.

She said, "Let's look for Vanessa." She hadn't said that name since last fall.

And in that moment I thought sadly of the level-headed woman Helen had tried to be, the kind who laminated recipes cut from newspapers, though I couldn't help but think of the so many other things my sister had been: the daredevil child; the contrite butter-fly killer; the teenager passed out on our ceramic-tile bathroom floor from downing a bottle of heart pills; and the hard shell, the empty insect husk.

I can't say I never wondered if she'd done it on purpose. A seed of dread had begun to germinate in me. I look at her from a thousand different angles, her thousand different selves, and I still don't know.

One thing I do know: when looking at the entirety of your life, you are at once every part of it. Watching her empty the trunk and peer into the cupholders, witnessing my sister 'look for Vanessa', I realize there is no shortage of Helens. Whatever contradictions she harbours within her infinite facets, she is an entity you could never understand by examining each individually. Somewhere along the curve of her millipede spine, Helen was still the girl who ate that butterfly's wings. She was at once capable of everything she had done, and nothing.

Christine de León
She stretches herself

She stretches herself
across two continents.
As her old country steeps in humidity, her new one freezes over.

Here is where the creases in her brown hands
chaff to match
the white frost that etches itself onto glass panes
in the grey, silent dawn.

She sweeps the floors and mops
the soiled bottoms of other people's children.
She daydreams of her own baby who lives
across two seas and an ocean.
Each Sunday at noon, she throws down her anchors
of colourful postcards and crackly phone calls.

She cooks healing recipes with ginger and aniseed
she picks over in Chinatown.
She spoons the fragrant soup
into pink, feverish mouths
that never suckled at her own breasts.

6000 miles away, her husband wagers a month's pay
on mahjong and coconut wine.

She washes lace underwear in soapy water,
rubbing out the period stains of a teenage girl,
wondering if her own child has become a woman yet.

Her hands are swollen, but she can still sew.
Her eyes falter, but she can still see a lie.
The lines in her face do not add up
to the crisp notes she counts out for a ticket
to the place she still calls *bayan ko*.

Jessica Waite
Whiteout

Content warning: emotional abuse
The buzzer sounds and I bound toward my teammates. We're a jumping, hugging cluster of ponytails. Jules throws her arm around my sweaty shoulders and raises her water bottle.

"Mikeeeey! Three-pointer for the win!" She sprays lemon–lime victory juice over us, feigning champagne. We shake hands with our rivals, accept the gold medals, kiss the plastic chalice.

The home team's coach, just defeated, shakes my hand and smiles as she awards me the medal for Tournament MVP. "Wish you played for me, kiddo."

I grin at her. "Thanks, Nancy."

"No showers, girls," barks our coach, Cal. "Grab your stuff and get to the van. On the road in ten. Eleven, and you walk."

Typical. We win him the championship, and he makes us ride five hours home with Gatorade in our hair. He's spiffed up in his black jeans and dress shirt, the top buttons open to show off a triangle of chest hair that Viv and I used to mock, gagging. No one makes Cal-jokes with me anymore. Locker room conversations often stop when I walk in, but right now all the girls are buzzing. I change into my tracksuit, stuff my uniform into my gym bag and walk back through the emptying gym. In the far corner, there's a shadow at the edge of the bleachers where I'll be able to stretch in relative privacy.

I lie on my back like a dead bug, holding the soles of my sock feet in my hands. My doctor assigned me thirty deep breaths in this position after every game so I don't end up back in his office with my belly-button askew from lumbar spasms. At least I've got time to stretch without having to jostle for a spot in the van. The back window's mine by seniority. Grade twelve should have meant sharing those backseat privileges with Viv and Tara, our shenanigans finally out of Cal's earshot. With them here, we'd have won in a blowout; without them, the narrow victory sinks in my stomach like a loss.

Viv cried when she told me she wasn't coming back to the team. "I'm so sorry, Mich. I'd play just for you, I really would, but I can't handle Cal anymore. Look at this." She lifted her blond curls and showed me a smooth patch of scalp the size of a quarter, just behind her ear. "My hair's falling out from stress. It's called alopecia. It's getting hard to hide." Viv's beautiful goldilocks, lased bare by Cal's cruel commentary. How many times had I stood frozen in practice, imagining myself slinking into the hardwood, hiding under the lines painted on the gym floor? "I get it, Vivver." I smoothed her hair and put my hand on her shoulder. "Don't let him turn you into a bald fucker like him."

I don't blame my friends for boycotting this season, but I miss them. If a provincial team sponsorship hadn't paid for my Air Jordans, I'd have spent last night celebrating Tara's eighteenth birthday, not sardined into a room at the Travelodge. I love my younger teammates, but I don't quite fit in with them. It's okay.

Dead bug position. Ten breaths to go. From my upside-down vantage point, I spot someone in our black-and-red team jacket moving behind the bleachers. I peer through the scaffolding to a maintenance corridor near the home-team's dressing room. I see an ass in too-tight Levi's, the back of a shiny head—it's Cal, wrapping the opposing coach, Nancy, in an intimate embrace. I saw their collegial handshake-hug at the end of our game. This is not that.

Oh, shit. I beeline toward the exit, dizzy from standing up too fast. I've almost made it out the metal doors, when I hear Cal shout, "Mikey—you're riding shotgun!"

Ugh. I jam my feet into my boots and step into the frozen January night. The falling snowflakes must be vaporizing before they even land on my hair. I'm a steamcloud stomping across the parking lot.

I do not want to spend the next five hours within spitting

distance of Cal. I'm still living with the consequences of my first time in the passenger seat, when he drove me back to our Winnipeg hotel to retrieve a forgotten sneaker. That dreadful day, two years ago, I'd been a rookie, too stupefied to lie.

"So, Michelle, does your mom have a boyfriend?"

"Huh? Ummm no ..."

"Cool. What kind of flowers does she like?"

"What? You mean, like, roses?"

When I got home from the tournament, I laughed about it.

"Hey, Mom—I think Cal's gonna ask you out."

Hilarious, to my teenage mind, that any woman would consider dating this short, bald man with his intense black stare, Adidas short-shorts and Rock'em Sock'em wristwatch. This goon who calls his football players by their girlfriend's names to make them tackle harder. *Get outta your comfort zone, ladies!* This power-tripping high school gym teacher, who'll kick you in the ass for bending over to tie your shoe. *Double knot 'em!*

I hadn't thought of my mom as lonely, just double-tired from working two jobs and raising two teenagers on her own. Dad had been incommunicado since we jumped ship, Mom pulling our lifeboat across a sea of empty bottles to relative safety. Five years of ramen noodles and solo parenting would cloud anyone's romantic judgement, right?

The van I'm about to get into will be parked in my driveway tonight, and the dude driving it will crawl into bed with my mom, one thin wall away from me.

If I'd understood Mom's thousand-yard stare, I'd have been quicker on my feet when Cal cornered me in the van that day. "Boyfriend? Oh yeah, she's totally devoted to Jim. Wish he'd lay off the 'roids though. He's already huge, and they make him super jealous."

I get into the passenger seat, pull out my book and a granola bar. Cal opens the driver's door. "Michelle! Shake the snow off your goddamn boots."

I open the door, smash my heels against the mud rail and slam it back closed.

Cal drives along Main Street to the junction. We turn south onto a single lane highway, no traffic in either direction. Snow swirls through the headlight beams. As we accelerate, snowflakes come at us in white lines of light, like we're a starship reaching warp-speed. The effect is mesmerizing, calming. I lean back into

171

my seat, grateful for the quiet.

It doesn't last.

"So, Nancy and I got together last night and did some scouting reports for the provincial team," Cal says, eyes forward.

Oh, jeez. A cover story? To a teenager? We invented lying about sex. It would never have even occurred to me that Nancy had been at our hotel last night. And what a lame smokescreen—I've been on the provincial team for three years. They don't scout in January.

"Was Nate there too?" Nancy and her husband Nate had coached me last summer.

"Don't be stupid, Michelle. Nate coaches their boys' team. They're in Saskatoon this weekend."

"Sorry." I clench my throat into a fake-sweet vocal filter. "It's just that Nate's such an awesome coach. He's the best coach I've ever met. He'd be such a great scout."

Cal says nothing, but I feel us accelerating. I look at the speedometer. 110 kph. He's driving too fast. The road is covered in wispy, drifting snow. I can't tell if the yellow line is striped or solid. It's not even obvious where the shoulder ends and the ditch begins. We're following faint tracks made by an earlier vehicle. My driving instructor had warned me about winter conditions; black ice could send us spiralling into the ditch. I check my seatbelt and look over my shoulder. The other girls are talking or doing homework by flashlight. Jules has her earbuds in and eyes closed. No one else seems to feel any sense of danger.

"You know," I say, "my mom really liked Nate when she met him last summer. She just loved his wavy hair." I don't look at Cal for a reaction. I stare into the white-lit snow.

Then the snow is gone. The view out the window is gone. Out the windshield there's only darkness.

I turn toward Cal. "Did you do that?" He doesn't answer.

By the faint glow of the dash light, I notice a hint of a smirk in the corner of his mouth. He's acting like everything is normal, but he's turned off the headlights. I look back at the other girls; still oblivious.

"Ha. Ha. Ha." *Wear a game face, like he insists. Don't let your opponent under your skin.* Inside, I can feel my heart pounding.

Cal steers the van to the left. We barrel blindly into the black. Speeding faster. In the wrong lane now. Does this clunker even have airbags? My hands grip the vinyl edges of my seat, and I watch for the lights of the truck that will hit us head-on. I can't see a thing.

I flash to the headline in tomorrow's paper: 'Highway Tragedy: Basketball Team Dies in Whiteout'. I hear people talking afterwards:

"… awful shame …"

"… their whole lives ahead of them … "

"… they died champions …"

No. If we die, it will be as hostages. The real headline: 'Psycho Coach Kills Innocents'.

Suddenly his reason is clear. I'd thought that he was trying to scare me into keeping silent, but it's not that. He's like the second-grader I babysit: flipping the checkerboard, sending red and black pieces flying, screaming, "I don't lose!"

Cal wants to intimidate me. He doesn't care about my mom. He just wants to win. I can save us all by surrendering.

Instead, I say, "I quit."

Cal jogs the steering wheel, veering back toward our lane for a quick second and then holding course in the wrong lane. We drive in dark silence for an infinite moment as I scan the distance for oncoming traffic. He's holding our lives at stake, like it's nothing. Like *we're* nothing. *What a motherfucker.* If I give in to him, I *will* be nothing. Fury rises from my belly and emerges as icy resolve.

"Kill us all if you want, but I'll never play basketball for you again." I'm surprised by how matter-of-fact my voice sounds. "Who'd come with me, if I asked them right now?" I gesture toward my teammates. "Which girl *won't* tell her parents if I scream?"

His foot comes off the accelerator. He understands. Somehow, he deflected staff-room questions about Viv's and Tara's departures, but my teachers know how invested my future is in this sport. If I leave the team, Cal will be on the hot seat. People will find out about this. He could be fired, and even if they keep him, he won't win another basketball tournament this year. We both know it.

He puts the lights on and steers us back into our lane. "You can't quit. You'll lose your scholarship."

"I don't care." I stare into the snow.

"You'll be off the Canada Games team."

"I don't care." I stare into the snow.

We go on like this, his every objection met with the same three syllables. My gaze doesn't waver. My life will look different without a scholarship, but my grades will get me into university. I can work part-time. I'm going to make it.

We stop for gas in a small town. Everyone files in to use the washroom. When I return to the van, I reclaim my window seat at the back.

It's after midnight when we pull into the school parking lot. Parents hug their victorious daughters, congratulate Cal with glove-handed pats on the back. I'm glad my mom's not here. She'll be sleeping, so I won't have to find words for her tonight.

Cal pulls into our cinder-block carport, and I notice the kitchen light is on. Mom's up. Cal will have to plug in the block heater so this old van will start in the morning. I hop out of the side door and hustle up the steps to get into the house before him.

Mom's sitting at the kitchen table in her burgundy bathrobe, a cigarette in her right hand. Her short dark hair is pushed up into sprigs, and her brown eyes are tired but smiling. "Couldn't sleep," she says, suppressing a yawn. "Heard the highways were bad. How was it?"

"Mom—" I put my hand on her shoulder, feeling the soft, warm velour. "We won."

Maryann Martin

There Were Moments

I did wonder about you, my colleague, friend,
fellow citizen of my years here, who debated the distance
from right to wrong, struggled with the difference
between speaking and being heard. I watched you
with interest, fortified by the times you came to me
with your insights. But there were the pretenses,
storms of their own variety, leaving this disrupted
landscape in their wake. During the months
when you thought me so different from yourself,
I sympathized with the buttercups trodden in haste,
all the live bait hooked by hurried hands. Still, for a time
we spent our days side by side among the rocks
and trees of this shore and I came to understand
that all you really wanted was to feel that blessing
of connection. But the gales, vicious, merciless, whipped us
up and down the shoreline. Now here we are, each our own take
on relentless, with the boat that once held us splintered
across the beach. We walk along, you choosing your way,
me making mine. I face the incoming tide, grateful
for our arrival, curious about the people we're becoming,
the many shells crushed smooth, sparkling in the sand.

Ellen Adams

a cracked foundation at grandma's house

resilience is the smell of
must

in the basement

we're still cleaning

Contributors

Alan Hill grew up with a brother with schizophrenia, which has been the most formative influence on his writing. Alan is the former Poet Laureate of the City of New Westminster, British Columbia. Through his work with survivors of the mental health system, he has come to believe in the transformative and revolutionary power of the literary arts.

Alejandra Jimenez de Luis is a Spanish Canadian historian and poet whose work focuses mainly on place, memory and mythology. She can often be found drinking tea at three in the morning.

Alex Benarzi is a writer, editor and educator residing in Calgary, Alberta. Alex has a visual impairment due to a rare genetic condition. While it was thought he would never be able to read, he defiantly dove into the literary world at a young age. Voracious reading turned into voracious writing as he honed his craft. Alex received a Bachelor's in English from Queen's University in 2010 and a Bachelor of Education in 2011. Alongside teaching, Alex continues to improve his skills as a writer. His work of flash faction, 'Men, Mice, and Trees' was published by freeze frame fiction in 2017, and his short story 'Nerium' was published in the Coffin Hop Press anthology, *Baby, It's Cold Outside*.

Allison Thompson is a transgender artist and writer living in Edmonton, Alberta. Allison is best known for writing whimsically themed stories with dark undertones. A fun story about a fruit-powered robot becomes a story about seeking comfort from an abuser. A tale based on hippos eating marbles is transformed into a Cold War class struggle. She loves conducting excessive research for stories and has led a challenging and varied life. These factors and more contribute to Allison's unique voice.

Alycia Pirmohamed is a Canadian-born poet living and studying in Scotland. Her chapbook *Faces that Fled the Wind* was selected by Camille Rankine for the BOAAT Chapbook Prize. Other awards include the CBC Poetry Prize, 92/Y Discovery Poetry Contest, the Ploughshares Emerging Writer's Contest in Poetry, the Adroit Journal Djanikian Scholars program, and the Gulf

Coast Poetry Prize. Alycia's work has appeared in publications internationally, including *The Paris Review, Prairie Schooner, Best Canadian Poetry 2019* and *PRISM international*, among others. She has received support from The Royal Society of Literature, and from Calgary Arts Development via The City of Calgary.

Amanda Lederle is a Toronto-based artist and facilitator. Their artistic work uses the form of maps, inventory and list-making to explore the emotions involved in experiences such as anxiety, courage and self-care. Their ink hand drawings invite the viewer to consider where they are in their own journeys.

Ania Telfer belongs in the realm of abstraction and spirit. She finds spiritual inspiration in the Baha'i Faith and believes that all art is worship of the Divine. Her work has been shown across Canada and is held in many private collections worldwide.

Brandie J. Wright is a photographer located in Calgary, Alberta. She loves creating pictures of the night sky, landscapes and wildlife. Her location and love of travel allows her to explore a variety of unique landscapes under the sun and stars. Through her images, she seeks to reconnect us with our natural world and explore what we often overlook. Brandie is a storyteller by nature: when she isn't behind the lens, she is behind the computer screen working as a professional communicator.

Chelsea Welsh is a Scottish poet and editor from the outskirts of Edinburgh whose work can be found online and in print. She teaches English and co-founded The Selkie Publications CIC in 2018 after completing a Master's in Creative Writing from The University of Edinburgh.

Christa Marie Burgin is an emerging author and editor based in the New York City area. She holds a Master's with merit in Creative Writing from The University of Edinburgh and a Bachelor's (cum laude) in English and Psychology from St. Lawrence University. She works as an editor for Prescient Healthcare Group, and as Head of Prose for The Selkie Publications CIC. Her writing can be found in *From Arthur's Seat, Inciting Sparks, Every Hundred Feet: Tales of Laurentians Abroad, The Laurentian Magazine* and *The St. Lawrence Review*. She has also worked as an editor for *The Selkie*, *Inciting Sparks*, *The Laurentian Magazine* and *The St. Lawrence Review*. While her work is most often based in the new adult genre, she is equally drawn to and inspired by speculative and dystopian fiction and narrative nonfiction.

Christine de León was born in Toronto to Filipino parents who fled the Marcos regime. She is a freelance writer with an early career as a dancer and performance artist. Her work has been shown in Toronto, New York, Berlin and London, where she now resides.

Eimear Laffan lives in Nelson, British Columbia. Her work has appeared in *Ambit*, *Wildness* and *MoonPark Review*.

Ellen Adams is a permanent resident of Canada. Ellen's work has appeared in *Kenyon Review*, *Black Warrior Review*, *Ploughshares* and elsewhere. She is a Lambda Literary Fellow, a Ploughshares Emerging Writer and a grantee of the Elizabeth George Foundation and Canada Council for the Arts. Her writing is listed as notable in the 2019 collection of *Best American Essays*. She has been awarded residencies at The Banff Centre, Hedgebrook and Helene Wurlitzer Foundation of New Mexico.

Finnian Burnett wears a lot of hats. The Director of Education for the non-profit Golden Crown Literary Society (GCLS), she also runs the GCLS Writing Academy. Finnian teaches college English and early British Literature and is a doctoral student at Murray State University. She has published five books with Sapphire Publishing. Her sixth book, *Coyote Ate the Stars* (2018), won first place in Fantasy in the Writer's Digest Self-Published Book Awards. She has won two Rainbow Awards, but her claim to fame is writing her books with a twenty-pound cat on her forearms. Finnian lives in British Columbia with her wife and pets.

Heather Bonin MacIntosh grew up in moose country with her lifelong friend, Vicki. She writes stories that share cultures and celebrate our diversity. Her work has been published in the *Blood is Thicker* anthology, *Westword* and *LaVaLab* e-zine. She lives in Calgary with her husband and daughters.

Heidi Klaassen writes fiction and nonfiction. She holds a Bachelor's in Criminology and a Certificate in Creative Writing from the University of Calgary and is currently pursuing the Professional Editing Standards Certificate from Queen's University. Heidi works as the Program Coordinator for the Alexandra Writers' Centre Society and side hustles as designer/maker for her eco-friendly label, Hekkal & Hyde. She lives in Calgary with her husband, sons and rescue chihuahuas. 'The Anvil' is the story of Heidi's journey through chronic pain, organ removal and pharmaceutical dependence. She awaits her fourth surgery for this condition.

Holly Schofield travels through time at the rate of one second per second, oscillating between the alternate realities of city and country life. The author of over 80 short stories, her works are used in university curricula and have been translated into several languages. Her stories have appeared in *Analog Science Fiction and Fact*, *Lightspeed*, *Escape Pod*, the Aurora-winning anthology *Second Contacts* and many other publications throughout the world. She hopes to save the world through science fiction and homegrown heritage tomatoes.

Jessica Waite lives in Calgary, Alberta. She writes to reconcile the great mysteries of the universe with the small mysteries of her own life, like how the same cluster of dog hair keeps re-appearing under her chair week after week. Jessica knows that writing heals. She helps others use narrative to transform grief and sorrow into meaning. Her essays and short stories have been published in the Unites States, Canada and online.

Kailash Srinivasan is a graduate of the UBC Creative Writing MFA program and lives in Vancouver. His work has appeared in *The Coachella Review*, *Antilang*, *Oyster River Pages*, *Sidereal*, *Queen Mob's Teahouse*, *Bad Nudes*, *Lunch Ticket*, *OxMag*, *Going Down Swinging*, *Regime*, *Tincture* and others. He has been shortlisted for Into the Void Fiction Prize and longlisted for the Bath Short Story Award and Bristol Short Story Prize.

Katherine Koller writes for stage, screen and page. Her plays include *Coal Valley*, *The Seed Savers* and *Last Chance Leduc*, which won the Alberta Playwriting Competition. Excerpts from

181

her opera, *The Handless Maiden*, played in Vancouver and Hope Soup, for radio, and was recorded at the Edmonton Fringe in 2019. *Art Lessons*, her debut novel, was a finalist for both the Edmonton Book Prize and the Alberta Readers' Choice Award. Her collection of short stories about second chances, *Winning Chance*, won a High Plains Book Award.

K. R. Byggdin is an alum of the Writers' Federation of Nova Scotia's Alistair MacLeod Mentorship Program and the Banff Centre's Emerging Writers Intensive. Their writing has won the Sheldon Currie Fiction Prize by *The Antigonish Review* and has also appeared in *Grain*, *The Quilliad* and elsewhere. Born and raised on the Prairies, they now live in Kjipuktuk (Halifax).

Kristin Bjornerud is a visual artist based in Montréal, Québec. Born in Alberta in 1980, she received her BFA with Honours from the University of Lethbridge in 2002 and her MFA from the University of Saskatchewan in 2005. Her work, which has been exhibited nationally, is represented in numerous public collections, including the Canada Council Art Bank, the Saskatchewan Arts Board and the Bank of Montréal. Kristin has received grants from the Canada Council for the Arts, the Saskatchewan Arts Board, the Ontario Arts Council and the Conseil des arts et des lettres du Québec.

Ky Mason is a Saskatchewan born and raised queer poet and spoken word artist, working and living on Treaty 6 in Saskatoon. His work focuses on healing, personal experience and his queerness. Community and youth opportunities are important to him; he organizes Write Out Loud youth poetry shows in Saskatoon and is on the organizing committee for the Voices of Today youth poetry festival, held yearly in Toronto. He has been published in *The Sheaf* and *In Medias Res* and has self-published two chapbooks. He has also been on the Write Out Loud slam team twice, before becoming an organizer, and on the Tonight It's Poetry adult slam team in 2019.

Lexie Angelo holds a Master's with Distinction in Creative Writing from The University of Edinburgh. She has been published internationally, and her debut chapbook titled *A Rough Season* was released in 2020 by Loft on Eighth Press. She is the Chief

Editor of The Selkie Publications CIC and teaches writing at the University of Calgary.

Marina Stepanova, June Summer Jones, Siegfried Jerusalem, John G. Carmody, Ron Romanowski and Ruth Rachel Cyprian are six non-binary writers working in their person to form the New Festival Theory crew. Their persona Ron Romanowski has been designated to handle their administrative affairs. They have published two books: *The Big Book of Canadian Poetry* (Augustine Head Press, 2011) and *Incantations From the Republic of Fire* (2013), and they continue to work on poetry in the rich ground of one of North America's most diverse cultures, Winnipeg, Canada.

Maryann Martin was awarded an Alistair MacLeod Mentorship in poetry by the Writers' Federation of Nova Scotia and was a poetry finalist in the 35th Atlantic Writing Competition. Her poems have recently appeared in Canadian literary magazines like *The New Quarterly, Arc* and *Grain*. Her work is featured in *Halifax* (2016), published by Frog Hollow Press in Victoria, British Columbia.

Moni Brar is an uninvited settler on unsurrendered territories of the Treaty 7 region and the Syilx of the Okanagan Nation. She is a Punjabi Sikh Canadian writer exploring diasporan guilt, identity, cultural oppression and intergenerational trauma. She believes in the possibility of healing through literature. Her work has appeared in *PRISM international, Hart House Review, Existere, The Maynard, Untethered* and other publications. She is a member of the Alexandra Writers' Centre Society, The League of Canadian Poets and the editorial board of *New Forum Magazine*.

Nadeen Almubarak is a writer and psychotherapist who was born and raised in Saudi Arabia and is now based in Ottawa, Canada. In her stories, she draws on the themes of immigrant experience, mental health and women's issues. Nadeen is interested in narratives that convey the complicated identities of Arab women. Her story 'Ghareeb' won first place in a creative writing contest conducted by *Muftah*. Her stories have appeared in *Jahanamiya* and *Muftah*.

Nicole Haywood considers art-making an integral spiritual and therapeutic practice where she exorcizes her most painful experiences and anxieties using intuitive drawing, painting and poetry. The components of these intuitive works are imbued with autobiographical significance and often recur and transform throughout her practice. The metaphorical threads contained in each motif shift in meaning as Nicole's own relationship with herself is shifted and reframed by the passage of time and the accumulation of experience. Her practice is a process of continual self-reflection and an attempt to document the palimpsestic remnants of her own shape-shifting personal mythologies.

Pamela Medland is a Calgary poet whose work explores the intersection of place, time and personal narrative. You can find her poetry online and in print in literary journals and anthologies such as *FreeFall*, *Grain*, *Room* and most recently *We Are One: Poems from the Pandemic*. Pamela's poem 'Dust' won the 2020 Word on the Lake Writing Contest, while 'In the Loggia dei Lanzi' won top prize for the Poetry & Prose category of the SAAG Arts Writing Prize 2020 Arts Writing Contest. Pamela is a contributing editor for *Arc Poetry Magazine*.

Pranisha Shrestha is an illustrator and animation designer living in Victora, BC. Originally from Kathmandu, Nepal, Pranisha holds a Bachelor's and Master's in Animation from India. She recently completed a Master's in Illustration from Edinburgh, Scotland. She has used both print and digital media for historical visual narratives, interactive media visual designs and biographical illustrations.

Rayanne Haines's writing has appeared in *Fiddlehead*, *Impact: The Lives of Women After Concussion*, *Voicing Suicide: A Poetry Anthology*, *FreeFall*, *Lida Literary Magazine*, *Wax Poetry and Arts*, *Funicular Magazine* and *Indefinite Space*, among others. She is the host of the literary podcast An Eloquent Bitch and is the Alberta Northwestern Territories Representative for the League of Canadian Poets. Rayanne is an Edmonton Artist Trust Fund Award recipient. Her poetry and prose have been short-listed for the Canadian Authors Association Exporting Alberta Award and the John Whyte Memorial Essay Alberta Literary

Award. Her work focuses on the female narrative, mental health and intergenerational female trauma.

Robin van Eck is a Calgary writer whose work has appeared in numerous literary magazines and anthologies in Canada and the United States. Her first novel Rough was published by Stonehouse Publishing in 2020. When she's not writing, Robin works as the Executive Director for the Alexandra Writers' Centre.

Sam Le Butt is an editor and writer based in Tokyo, Japan. She holds a Master's with Distinction in Creative Writing from The University of Edinburgh, and is the Chief Editor at The Selkie Publications CIC. Her writing explores the intersection of feminism, bodies, the uncanny and the environment. Her short fiction can be found at *Cephalo Press* and in anthologies *From Arthur's Seat 3* and *Roten*. Her short story collection *Curious Women and Other Creatures* was published in 2021 by Radical Bookshop.

Shannon Taylor-Jones is an emerging Canadian artist working in Toronto and London, Ontario. She obtained a BFA with a major in Drawing and Painting from OCAD University in 2016, and a postgraduate certificate from Centennial College in Museum and Cultural Management in 2018. Her work focuses on abstraction and explores the ideas of intuition, process and materiality. She is a current resident artist at Good Sport, an art collective, gallery and studio space in London, Ontario.

Sindhu Rajasekaran is a literary nomad, seeker and feminist. Trained as an engineer, she became a writer and obtained a Master's in Creative Writing from The University of Edinburgh. Her first novel *Kaleidoscopic Reflections* was nominated for the Crossword Book Award. It chronicled the travails of an inter-caste Tamil family trying to navigate its identity in a caste-ridden India. Her second book is a collection of edgy short stories about femininity titled *So I Let It Be*, published by Pegasus Publishers, United Kingdom. Sindhu's work has appeared in the *Asia Literary Review*, *Kitaab*, *Muse India*, *The Swaddle*, *Gaysi*, *Bella Caledonia* and *Elsewhere Lit*. Sindhu is also a communications strategist and filmmaker. She produced a critically acclaimed

Indo-British feature film *Ramanujan*. She lives in Vancouver, Canada.

Sonali Misra is an Indian author of the nonfiction book *21 Fantastic Failures: and what their stories teach us* (Rupa Publications, 2020). Her short stories and personal essays have appeared in *So Hormonal* (Monstrous Regiment Publishing, 2020), *#Horror* (Scholastic India, 2018), *From Arthur's Seat 3* (2018) and elsewhere. Her novel excerpt was shortlisted for Hachette UK's Grow Your Story program in 2020. Sonali is the Co-founder of The Selkie Publications CIC and was its Head of Fiction and New Voices Fiction Lead, 2017–2018. She is currently pursuing a PhD in Publishing Studies at the University of Stirling, UK, and heads the Society of Young Publishers Scotland as its Co-chair. She has worked in Indian publishing in editorial and sales (product) roles at organizations such as Scholastic and Hachette.

Suzanne Whitney Ghadimi is a Canadian Scottish writer originally from Montreal, Quebec. She lives in Aberdeenshire, Scotland. Suzanne holds a BFA in Studio from the Emily Carr University in Vancouver and graduated with an MLitt with Distinction in Creative Writing from the University of Aberdeen in 2018. Her first short story 'Pixies' was first published in *Causeway/Cabhsair*, a magazine of Irish and Scottish writing in 2019 and was then shortlisted for the Aesthetica Creative Writing Award 2019. Her short story 'The Rabbit' appears in *The Fairlight Book of Short Stories*, published in October 2020. A visual artist, ceramicist and writer, Suzanne enjoys expressing her creative process in many varied mediums while exploring complex themes of interpersonal and intrapersonal relationships.

Tal Bressette is Anishinaabekwe, mother and grandmother, from southern Ontario and has been writing since she was a child to try to make sense of her world. Her people come from a tradition of oral storytelling and teachings. The written language (English) was not trusted, as her grandfather once told her, because it had so often been used against her people. Tal writes to bridge these two disconnected realities. To capture a moment that is true and to see herself and her reality in the words.

Taliha Quadri is a freelance proofreader based in the United Kingdom. She enjoys reading and creating digital art to unwind. She has a Bachelor's in English Language and Literature from the University of Hertfordshire and a Master's in Creative Writing from The University of Edinburgh. She co-founded The Selkie Publications CIC in 2018 and was its Editor-in-Chief until 2019; she is now the Managing Director and Publisher.

Tristan Hay Lee's short story 'The Party on Olympus' was a winner of the 2017 TCTE Short Fiction Contest. A staged reading of her one-act play *Birdwatching* was performed at the 34th Annual Brave New Play Rites Festival in 2020. Born and raised in Toronto, she comes from a diverse background of Korean, Japanese and Scottish heritage.

Vina Nguyen's writings have found homes in *Every Day Fiction*, *The Selkie* and *FEED*. 'The Sleeping Towers' is a recent winner of the Flash Fiction Contest conducted by *Lida Literary Magazine*. She's crafted two EPs with her trip-hop x pop band, Vina After Dark; writes moody, surreal novels; and wants to eat fewer potato chips.

Willow Loveday Little is a writer, poet and freelance editor whose work has appeared in places like *The Dalhousie Review*, *yolk*, *Lantern Magazine* and *On Spec*. She holds a Bachelor of Arts from McGill University.

Zachary Keesey got back into creative writing after an unnecessarily long hiatus. He has worked in Education for six years, which has allowed him to teach at K-12 and university levels in Japan, the United States and Canada.